Contents

PAGE 26

Did you 'ear the one about the mouse?

PAGE 42

Food of the future

PAGE 158

Living medicines

PAGE 204

Free-fall thrill

PAGE 229

Life before birth

Welcome to Collins GCSE Science!

This book has been written by teachers who are also experienced examiners. We hope you will find it gives you an insight into the fascinating world of Science. We have tried to make things relevant for you and your life in today's world. Science opens many gateways to exciting careers and further studies.

USING THIS BOOK

What you should know

Think back to what you have already learnt for GCSE Science. You need to remember and understand this work as your teacher will now develop it, explaining things in more detail.

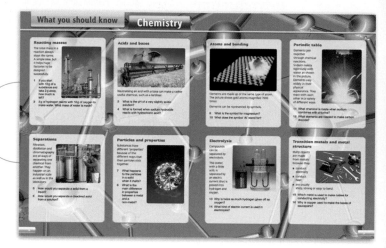

Module opener

This is designed to get you thinking about one or two of the important aspects of the module.

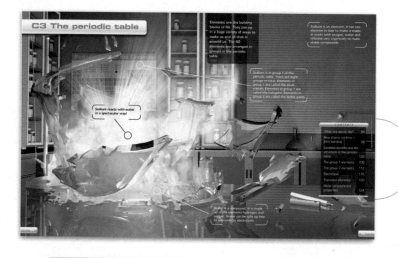

Main content

The main content is presented in three, coloured columns. Students entering foundation tier should understand the work in the green and blue columns. Higher tier students should concentrate on the blue and purple columns. Throughout the book, watch out for some fascinating facts that you might be able to include in your answers to examination questions, or in any coursework you do. There are also examples of common misunderstandings that examiners often find on examination papers.

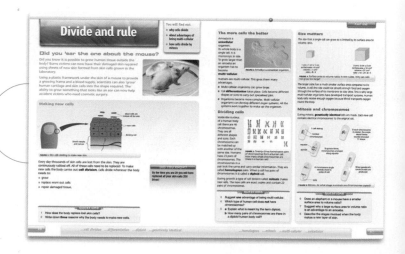

OCR GATEWAY

SCIENCE

FOR OCR GCSE ADDITIONAL SCIENCE B

AVALANCHE RESEARCH

Chris Sherry SERIES EDITOR
Colin Bell
Louise Smiles
Ann Daniels
Dave Berrington
Sandra Mitchell
Edmund Walsh

William Collins' dream of knowledge for all began with the publication of his first book in 1819. A self-educated mill worker, he not only enriched millions of lives, but also founded a flourishing publishing house. Today, staying true to this spirit, Collins books are packed with inspiration, innovation and a practical expertise. They place you at the centre of a world of possibility and give you exactly what you need to explore it.

Collins. Freedom to teach.

Published by Collins
An imprint of HarperCollinsPublishers
77–85 Fulham Palace Road
Hammersmith
London
W6 8JB

Browse the complete Collins catalogue at
www.collinseducation.com

© HarperCollinsPublishers Limited 2006

10 9 8 7 6 5

ISBN-13 978 0 00 721635 2
ISBN-10 0 00 721635 1

British Library Cataloguing in Publication Data. A Catalogue record for this publication is available from the British Library

Commissioned by Kate Haywood and Cassandra Birmingham

Publishing Manager Michael Cotter

Project managed by Nicola Tidman

Exam questions written by Dr Martin Barker, Lesley Owen and Karen Nicola Thomas

Glossary written by Gareth Price

Edited by Camilla Behrens

Proofread by Anita Clark

Internal design by JPD

Page make-up by IFADesign Ltd

Picture research by Caroline Thompson

Illustrations by IFADesign Ltd and Bob Lea

Cover artwork by Bob Lea

Cover design by John Fordham

Production by Natasha Buckland

Printed and bound by Martins the Printers, Berwick upon Tweed

Acknowledgements

The Publishers gratefully acknowledge the following for permission to reproduce copyright material. Whilst every effort has been made to trace the copyright holders, in cases where this has been unsuccessful or if any have inadvertently been overlooked, the Publishers will be pleased to make the necessary arrangements at the first opportunity.

The publishers would like to thank the following for permission to reproduce photographs (T = Top, B = Bottom, C = Centre, L = Left, R = Right):

Actionplus/Glyn Kirk, p179;
Alamy/Stuart Abraham, p41TL, Edward Parker, p75C, Lyndon Beddoe, p3CB, p204C;
BBC Photo Library, p3T, p26;
Colin Bell, p54C, p57T, p58C, p58B, p59, p61, p62C, p65L, p68, p84C, p85, p87, p88T;
British Red Cross Society /Mark Snelling, p79R;
Martyn Chillmaid, p148C;
Corbis/Michael Kim, p10TL, p178, Sam Greenwood/NewSport, p10TR, p183L, Colin Garratt/Milepost 92 ½, p10BL, p189R, p208, Roger Ressmeyer, p11TL, LWA-Dann Tardif/zefa, p34CB, Jim Richardson, p47CR, Martyn Goddard, p174, Royalty-Free, p186R, Paul Mounce, p187R, E. Klawitter/zefa, p189C, Paul Thompson/Eye Ubiquitous, p194L, Rick Gayle, p197T, David Madison/zefa, p205BR, Lake County Museum, p207, Jean-Philippe Arles/Reuters, pp212/213, Steve Raymer, p217B, West Semitic Research/Dead Sea Scrolls Foundation, p242R, DK Limited, p245T, Bettmann, p246T;
Charles E. Rotkin, p246B;
Tim Cuff, p75T;
Mary Evans Picture Library, p31, p151L;
FLPA/ Nigel Cattlin, p36C, p38, p41T, Gordon Roberts, p39T, Primrose Peacock, p47CL, Tui De Roy/Minden Pictures, p151R;
Ford Motor Company Limited, p182C, p188L;
Geophotos/Tony Waltham, p164;
Getty Images, p44T, The Image Bank, p16, Stone, p24BCR, p44CL, Taxi, p29, Altrendo, p182T;
Sally & Richard Greenhill Photo Library, p34C&B;
Courtesy of Guidant Corporation, p219R;
Hansen Ltd, p54T;
iStockphoto, p3C, p34T, p78, p79L, p96T, p96CT, p96L, p100L, p112T, p112BL, p124, p125L, p125C, p134T, p136B, p146, p158, p162, p163, p200R, p240T, p240B;
© 2006 Jupiterimages Corporation, p6TR, p7BR, p10BR, p34TC, p40, p48, p57C, p62R, p86, p88B, p175C, p176, p180, p181L, p183C, p185L, p187T, p192L, p192R, p197R, p201, p203, p204T, p205T, p206C, p211, p216, p217T, p218R, p220R;
Lynton & Lynmouth Cliff Railway, p206T;
Sandra Mitchell, p186T, 192T;
NASA, p200B;
NHPA/Ernie Janes, p33CL;
Philips Medical Systems, p219C;
Photolibrary, p181R, p192C, p217R, Phototake Inc, p7BL, pp12/13, p22C, p22B, p23T, p24CR, p27C, p33BC, p62L, p214R, p218T, p222T, p235, BSIP, p11BR, p228T, p231L, Raymond Blythe, p22T, Michael Richards, p32, Botanica, p33C, p39C, p44CR, p46, p62BC, Sinclair Stammers, p33BC/R, Robert Dowling, p41CR, Mark Hamblin, p65R, Harold Taylor, p65BR, Kathie Atkinson, p76CL, Index Stock Imagery, p193, p200T, p244T, Maximilian Stock Ltd, p220T;
Porsche Cars GB, p188C;
Sam Rentmeester / TU Delft, p194R;
The Roof Box Company, www.roofbox.co.uk, p202L;
Science Photo Library, p125R, p236T, p238C, Alfred Pasieka, pp8/9, p198L, Joe Tucciarone, pp10/11, Dr Najeeb Layyous, p3B, p6TL, p229, Andrew Syred, p6BR, Biophoto Associates, p7TL, Dr Jeremy Burgess, p7TR, p165, A. Barrington Brown, p14, Dr G Moscoso, p20, John Bavosi, p21, Eye of Science, pp52/53, p23C, p42C, Sidney Moulds, p55, Bo Veisland, MI&I, p6BL, p24T, Michael Abbey, p27T, Motta & Familiari / Anatomy Dept. / University "La Sapienza", Rome, p28CR, Steve Gschmeissner, p28BR, Ron Sutherland, p35, Ed Young/Agstock, p36T, Adam Hart-Davis, p36C, p175R, Cordelia Molloy, p3CT, p42TL, Volker Steger, p42T, J.C. Revy, p63, David Nunuk, p66, Thomas Dodge/Agstock, p8TR, p76T, p142T, Curt Maas /Agstock, p76CR, Scott Sinklier /Agstock, p77, Hank Morgan, p81, p231C, Robert Brook, p84T, p112BR, p148L, p168, p221TL, Philippe Plailly, p9TL, p94, Andrew Lambert Photography, p11TR, p96R, p96BL, p106C, p108C, p108R, p113T, p113CL, p114T, p114CL, p114CR, p122C, p123, p128, p135, p139, p166, p222R, Martyn F. Chillmaid, p9BR, p106T, p120, p121, p142B, p233, p236R, Charles D. Winters, p8BR, p9BL, p9TR, p100R, p107C, p110, p113CR, p114C, p117, p122B, p136C, p145, p160T, Laguna Design, p101, pp132/133, Dr P. Marazzi, p107T, David Taylor, p108L, David McCarthy, p112BC, G. Muller, Struers Gmbh, p126, David Parker, p127, Gusto, p134B, Rosenfeld Images Ltd, p136L, Peter Bowater, p8TL, p149, Tek Image, p157, Maximilian Stock Ltd, p8BL, p159, Sinclair Stammers, p160B, CNRI, pp172/173, Ton Kinsbergen, p185R, Spencer Grant, p194C, David Weintraub, p195T, G. Brad Lewis, p195L, Martin Bond, p195R, p247, TRL Ltd, p196T, Kairos, Latin Stock, p196R, Raymond Blythe, Sally McCrae Kuyper, p197L, Jeremy Walker, p202C, John A Ey III, p214T, Edward Kinsman, p215, Michael Donne, p219T, Alex Bartel, p221R, p245B, Sheila Terry, p225, Merlin Tuttle, p226, BSIP, Boucharlat, p228C, CC Studio, p232, Simon Fraser / NCCT, Freeman Trust, Newcastle-upon-Tyne, p234, Astrid & Hanns-Frieder Michler, p237, C. Powell, P. Fowler & D. Perkins, p238T, N. Feather, p239, John Howard, p240R, George Bernard, p242T, Gianni Tortoli, p242L, Larry Miller, p243R, Novosti, p243L, Skyscan, p244B, p253;
Jean-Loup Charmet, p111, George Ranalli, p260B, p262B, p264B, p266B, p268B, 270B, p272B;
TRL, p199;
The ULSAB-Advanced Vehicle Concepts (ULSAB-AVC) project, American Iron and Steel Institute, p198R.

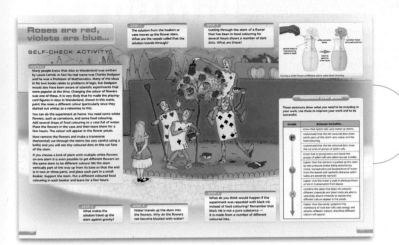

These activities give you an opportunity to find out how you are progressing through each module. You may be asked to work through this assessment for homework, or discuss and work with another student in the class who may assess you.

Module summary

At the end of each module, the key facts are summarised. There is also a quiz and an activity, to test your understanding. You could use these as a revision aid. Make sure that as you look at the key facts, you recall the content of the chapters in each module.

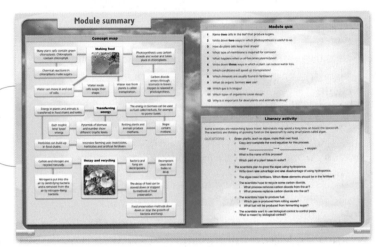

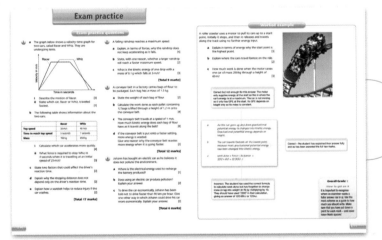

Exam practice

You may sit examinations at regular intervals during your course, or at the end of your course. One of the best ways to prepare for your examination is to practise answering examination questions. Learn from the example answers and mark schemes provided. In particular, be careful about the use of scientific language.

Skills assessment

In your examination papers, you will have to plot graphs, interpret data and understand scientific writings. Similar skills will be needed if you are to achieve high marks with coursework. Look at the examples of coursework you may be asked to do and make sure you understand how to gain the best marks you can.

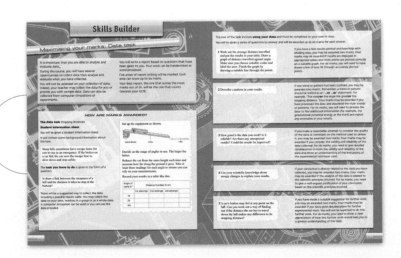

Cells and reproduction

Eggs and sperm are specialised cells.

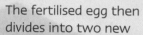

When the nucleus of an egg joins with the nucleus of a sperm fertilisation takes place.

The fertilised egg then divides into two new cells, then four, then eight and so on. The cells keep dividing to form an embryo. Once the embryo has formed arms and legs it is called a foetus.

The foetus then grows into a baby. To grow, a foetus needs food and oxygen. These are provided by the mother, via the placenta.

1   What is it called when the nucleus of an egg joins with the nucleus of a sperm?

2   Name **two** substances a foetus gets from its mother's placenta.

Growing up

The first part of life is childhood and the second is adolescence.

Adolescents go through a stage of life called puberty.

During puberty the following changes take place:

■ pubic hair grows
■ behaviour changes
■ boys grow hair on their faces
■ boys' voices deepen
■ girls' breasts develop
■ girls start to menstruate.

3   Write down **two** changes that happen to boys during puberty.

4   Write down **two** changes that happen to girls during puberty.

Blood and transport

The circulatory system moves substances around the body.

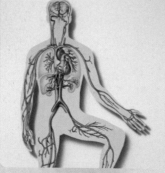

Oxygen is taken from the lungs to the body. Carbon dioxide is returned from the body to the lungs.

Arteries carry blood full of oxygen away from the heart. Veins carry blood without oxygen to the heart.

Blood is made up of red blood cells, white blood cells, plasma and platelets.

5   Write down the names of the **four** different parts of the blood.

6   Which blood vessels carry blood away from the heart?

Inheritance and selective breeding

Characteristics such as hair and eye colour are inherited from our parents.

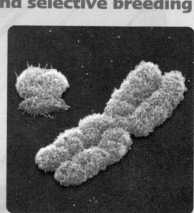

Characteristics are controlled by genes.

Genes are found on chromosomes inside the nucleus.

Selective breeding is when humans produce animals and plants that have desired characteristics. For example, cows are bred to produce more milk and crops are produced that are resistant to disease.

7   What do genes control?

8   Write down what is meant by the term 'selective breeding'.

Plant cells

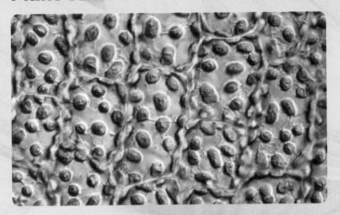

- Plant cells have strong walls for support.
- Chloroplasts are only found in plant cells.
- Most chloroplasts contain green pigments.
- Chloroplasts use light to make food.

9   Which parts of a plant cell are green?

10 What is used by chloroplasts to make food?

Photosynthesis

Plants use light to make biomass from carbon dioxide and water. The process is called photosynthesis.

Photosynthesis takes place inside chloroplasts.

Some of the food made in photosynthesis is stored as starch.

11 Which process takes place in chloroplasts?

12 Chloroplasts produce sugars. What are sugars made into so they can be stored in plant cells?

Uptake of water and minerals

Plants need water for photosynthesis. They also need minerals for healthy growth.

Plants absorb water and minerals from the soil through their root hairs.

13 What is absorbed from the soil by root hairs?

14 What do leaves use water for?

Plants and animals are interdependent

There is a great variety of plants and animals in different habitats.

Plants and animals depend on each other in many ways.

15 Which gas, produced by plants, is used by animals?

16 Which gas, produced by animals, is used by plants?

Reacting masses

The total mass in a reaction always stays the same. A simple idea, but it helps huge factories to be designed successfully.

1   If you start with 10 g of a substance and take 2 g away, how much is left?

2   2 g of hydrogen reacts with 16 g of oxygen to make water. What mass of water is made?

Acids and bases

Neutralising an acid with a base can make a rather useful chemical, such as a fertiliser.

3   What is the pH of a very slightly acidic solution?

4   What is formed when sodium hydroxide reacts with hydrochloric acid?

Separations

Filtration, distillation and chromatography are all ways of separating one chemical from another. They happen on an industrial scale as well as in the laboratory.

5   How would you separate a solid from a liquid?

6   How would you separate a dissolved solid from a solution?

Particles and properties

Substances have different 'properties' because of the different ways that their particles stick together.

7   What happens to the particles in a solid when it melts?

8   What is the main difference in properties between a metal and a non-metal?

Atoms and bonding

Elements are made up of the same type of atom. The picture shows gold atoms magnified 7000 times.

Elements can be represented by symbols.

9   What is the symbol for magnesium?

10 What does the symbol 'Al' stand for?

Periodic table

Elements join together through chemical reactions. Sodium reacts vigorously with water as shown in the picture. Elements vary widely in their physical appearance. They react with each other in a variety of different ways.

11 What chemical is made when sodium combines with chlorine?

12 What elements are needed to make carbon dioxide?

Electrolysis

Compounds can be separated by electrolysis.

This water, with a little acid, is separated by an electric current that is passed into hydrogen and oxygen.

13 Why is twice as much hydrogen given off as oxygen?

14 What kind of electric current is used in electrolysis?

Transition metals and metal structure

Many objects are made from metals because they:

■ conduct electricity

■ conduct heat

■ are usually shiny, strong or easy to bend.

15 Which metal is used to make cables for conducting electricity?

16 Why is copper used to make the bases of saucepans?

Speed and acceleration

$$\text{average speed} = \frac{\text{distance travelled}}{\text{time taken}}$$

$$\text{acceleration} = \frac{\text{change in speed}}{\text{time taken}}$$

Distance–time and speed–time graphs show how things move.

1   An athlete runs 800 m in 160 seconds. What is her average speed?

2   A car accelerates from 0 m/s to 20 m/s in 8 seconds. Find its acceleration.

Forces and motion

Forces can speed objects up or slow them down.

The bigger the force, the bigger the change in speed.

Force is measured in newtons (N).

3   What happens to a car when the driving force is bigger than the frictional force?

4   When all the forces acting on an object are balanced, what can you say about its motion?

Work, energy and power

Work is done whenever a force moves.

work done = force × distance moved

Energy is needed to do work.

All moving objects possess kinetic energy.

Work and energy are measured in joules (J).

Power is measured in watts (W).

$$\text{power (in watts)} = \frac{\text{energy transferred}}{\text{time taken}}$$

5   Name a device that converts electrical energy to light energy.

6   Sam transfers 500 J of energy in 20 seconds. Find her power.

Falling safely

All objects near Earth fall due to gravity.

Gravity makes them accelerate.

7   A 1 kg mass accelerates at 10 m/s^2 when dropped. What is the acceleration of a 2 kg mass when it is dropped from the same height?

8   What happens to the speed of a free-fall parachutist when his parachute opens?

Electrostatics

Electric charges on insulating materials cannot move. This is called static electricity.

There are two kinds of charge – positive and negative.

Like charges repel, unlike charges attract.

9 a What happens when two positively charged balloons are brought near each other?
 b Why does the cat's fur stand on end in the photo?
10 Which of these are electrical insulators?

copper   **wood**   **iron**
polythene   **brass**   **glass**

Current electricity

A complete loop is needed for a circuit to work.

Resistors can be used to change the current flowing in a circuit.

Electric charges on conductors move, producing an electric current. An electric current is a flow of electric charge.

A battery or power supply provides energy to move the electric charges.

Resistors can be connected in series or in parallel.

11 a Draw a circuit to show one cell and two lamps connected **i** in series and **ii** in parallel.
 b In which circuit would the lamps be brighter?
12 a What unit is used to measure electric current?
 b What unit is used to measure voltage?

Using electricity safely

An earthed conductor cannot become live.

Fuses and circuit breakers give protection if a fault occurs.

L = live (brown)

N = neutral (blue)

E = earth (green and yellow stripe)

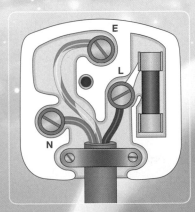

13 Why is it dangerous to touch an electricity supply with wet hands?
14 What happens to the wire inside a fuse if the current is too high?

Ultrasound

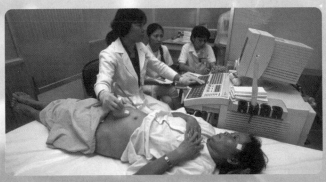

Ultrasound is sound with a pitch too high for humans to hear (above 20 000 Hz).

Sound cannot travel in a vacuum.

Reflection of sound is called an echo.

Reflection of ultrasound is used to produce a scan of a foetus to check that it is healthy.

15 Why can sound not travel in a vacuum?
16 What is meant by the 'frequency' of a sound?

In the race to fertilise the egg, only one sperm out of the million released can be successful.

...must be fertilised by a sperm.

...divides many times to produce all the cells in the human body.

In order to make a baby,
the human egg...

...takes 9 months to develop from a single cell to a baby.

Molecules of life

You will find out:
- about the structure of cells
- about chromosomes and DNA
- how genes code for proteins

The secret of life

In 1953 two men walked into the Eagle pub in Cambridge and announced, 'We have found the secret of life.'

They were Francis Crick and James Watson and they had just discovered the structure of DNA (deoxyribonucleic acid). They had worked out that a DNA molecule is shaped like a double helix.

Crick and Watson with their model of part of a DNA molecule.

What's in a cell?

An animal cell has the following parts.

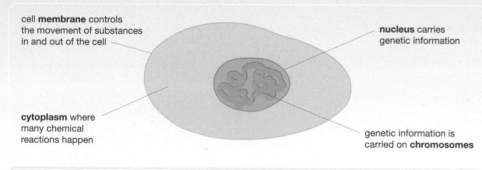

cell **membrane** controls the movement of substances in and out of the cell

nucleus carries genetic information

cytoplasm where many chemical reactions happen

genetic information is carried on **chromosomes**

FIGURE 1: An animal cell.

WOW FACTOR!

Jurassic Park could happen! Scientists plan to store DNA of animals facing extinction, so they can be recreated in the future.

Watch Out Animal cells don't have a cell wall – they have a cell membrane. Remember your skin is soft, not hard like a stem!

DNA code

DNA is a chemical found inside the nucleus. It forms structures called chromosomes. A section of a chromosome is called a **gene**. Each gene is a code for making **proteins**. Our bodies need to make proteins to grow and to repair cells.

Everyone has his or her own unique **DNA code**.

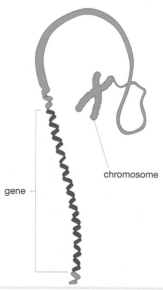

chromosome

gene

FIGURE 2: Each chromosome carries many genes.

QUESTIONS

1   Match up each part of the cell with the job it does.

Part of cell	Job
nucleus	where chemical reactions take place
cell membrane	carries genetic information
cytoplasm	controls movement of substances in and out of the cell

2   Which part of the nucleus carries coded information called genes?

3   Why does a cell need to make proteins?

...base code ...bases ...chromosome ...cytoplasm ...DNA ...DNA code ...DNA replication

Mitochondria

Cell respiration is carried out inside **mitochondria**. During respiration energy is released from glucose in the presence of oxygen.

DNA

DNA is split into sections called genes. Each gene holds the code for making a protein our bodies need, using amino acids from the food we eat. Proteins are made by joining amino acids into a chain. The DNA controls the order of amino acids in a protein. The production of proteins is called **protein synthesis**.

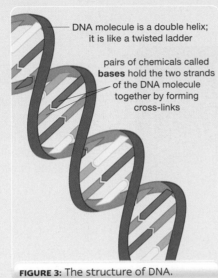

DNA molecule is a double helix; it is like a twisted ladder

pairs of chemicals called **bases** hold the two strands of the DNA molecule together by forming cross-links

FIGURE 3: The structure of DNA.

The structure of DNA helps it to copy itself every time a cell divides. When DNA makes a copy it is called **DNA replication**.

In 1985, scientist Alex Jeffreys developed a way of using DNA to identify people, called 'DNA fingerprinting'. The process produces a pattern of bands, like a barcode, which is unique.

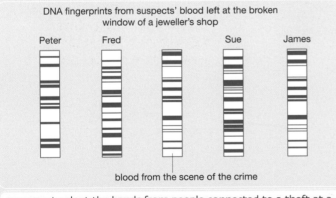

DNA fingerprints from suspects' blood left at the broken window of a jeweller's shop

Peter   Fred   Sue   James

blood from the scene of the crime

FIGURE 4: Look at the bands from people connected to a theft at a jeweller's shop. Who stole the jewels?

QUESTIONS

4   Suggest **one** reason why muscle cells have a lot of mitochondria.

5   From where does the body get its supply of amino acids?

6   Explain how DNA can be used to catch a thief.

7   What does a gene code for?

DNA replication

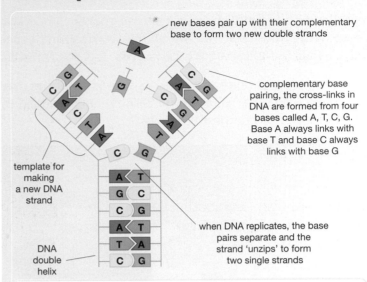

new bases pair up with their complementary base to form two new double strands

complementary base pairing, the cross-links in DNA are formed from four bases called A, T, C, G. Base A always links with base T and base C always links with base G

template for making a new DNA strand

when DNA replicates, the base pairs separate and the strand 'unzips' to form two single strands

DNA double helix

FIGURE 5: DNA replication. The double strand 'unzips' and two new double strands are formed.

Protein synthesis

The order of bases found in a section of DNA is called the **base code**. Each three bases code for an amino acid. For example, the sequence 'CAA' codes for the amino acid called valine. Cells use these base codes to join amino acids together in the correct order. If an amino acid is missing from the diet, the liver can change other amino acids into those that are needed.

DNA fingerprinting

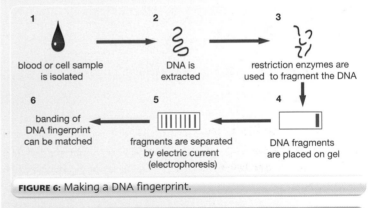

1 blood or cell sample is isolated
2 DNA is extracted
3 restriction enzymes are used to fragment the DNA
6 banding of DNA fingerprint can be matched
5 fragments are separated by electric current (electrophoresis)
4 DNA fragments are placed on gel

FIGURE 6: Making a DNA fingerprint.

QUESTIONS

8   The body needs 20 different amino acids to make proteins. Explain why we do not need to eat all 20.

9   How many amino acids are coded for in the following section of DNA?

AAATATCTCCCCTCAACCGGGCGGTAAATG

10   Write down the complementary base sequence for the section of DNA in **Q9**.

11   Describe how a DNA fingerprint is produced.

Making cheese

Simon and his friend Nisha visit a cheese-maker. Simon knows that cheese can be made from sour milk. When milk turns sour it separates into a solid and a liquid. The solid part is called **curds**. It is the curds that form cheese.

The chemical reaction that turns milk sour is slow. The cheese-makers tell Simon and Nisha that an **enzyme** called rennin is added to the milk. Enzymes speed up chemical reactions.

FIGURE 7: Making cheese. What is added to milk to speed up the souring reaction?

You will find out:

- how enzymes speed up reactions
- what changes the rate of enzyme reactions
- about the 'lock and key' mechanism

DID YOU KNOW?

There are enzymes under your kitchen sink! Household products, such as clothes washing detergents, use enzymes to speed up the breaking down of stains.

QUESTIONS

12 Name **one** example of an enzyme.

13 What do enzymes do to chemical reactions?

...*active site* ...*catalyst* ...*curds* ...*denatured* ...*enzyme* ...*optimum pH*

Enzymes and rate of reaction

An enzyme is a biological **catalyst**. It is a protein that speeds up a biological reaction. Enzymes catalyse most chemical reactions occurring within cells, such as respiration, photosynthesis and protein synthesis. Each enzyme is **specific** to a **substrate**.

In an enzyme-catalysed reaction, substrate molecules are changed into **product** molecules.

Enzyme-controlled reactions are affected by:

- pH (measures the acidity of a solution)
- temperature.

pH

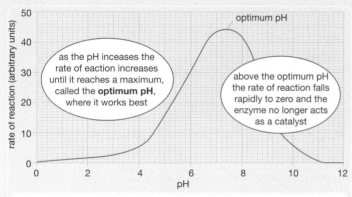

as the pH inceases the rate of eaction increases until it reaches a maximum, called the **optimum pH**, where it works best

optimum pH

above the optimum pH the rate of reaction falls rapidly to zero and the enzyme no longer acts as a catalyst

FIGURE 8: Graph to show how pH affects the rate of an enzyme-catalysed reaction. What is the optimum pH for this reaction?

Temperature

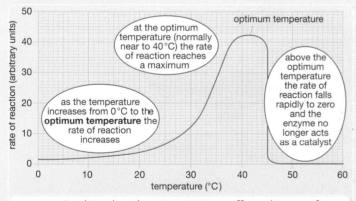

optimum temperature

at the optimum temperature (normally near to 40 °C) the rate of reaction reaches a maximum

as the temperature increases from 0 °C to the **optimum temperature** the rate of reaction increases

above the optimum temperature the rate of reaction falls rapidly to zero and the enzyme no longer acts as a catalyst

FIGURE 9: Graph to show how temperature affects the rate of an enzyme-catalysed reaction. Suggest why an enzyme ceases to function above approximately 40 °C.

QUESTIONS

14 What other name is given to enzymes?

15 Describe how changing the temperature changes the rate of an enzyme-catalysed reaction.

16 What is meant by the term optimum pH?

How enzymes work – the lock and key theory

Each enzyme has a unique sequence of amino acids. This results in each enzyme having a different shape. Within this shape is a structure called an **active site**. Only one type of substrate can fit into the active site making enzymes specific to a reaction. Once the substrate is attached to the active site it is turned into a product. The enzyme is like a lock and the substrate a key.

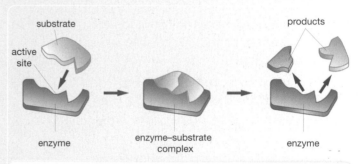

substrate

products

active site

enzyme

enzyme–substrate complex

enzyme

FIGURE 10: The lock and key theory of enzymes. How does the theory explain the specificity of enzymes?

Denaturing enzymes

If the shape of an enzyme changes it can no longer catalyse a reaction. The enzyme has become denatured. The substrate can no longer fit into the active site. An enzyme can be **denatured** by the following.

- Extremes of pH. Each enzyme has an optimum pH at which it works most efficiently. At this pH, the active site and the substrate molecule are a perfect fit. The further away from this pH, the more the enzyme molecule distorts and the less perfect the fit is. Eventually the substrate can no longer fit the active site and the enzyme stops working.

- High temperatures. As the temperature increases, the molecules gain more energy. More collisions occur and the rate of reaction increases. Above the optimum temperature, the enzyme denatures and the reaction stops.

QUESTIONS

17 Biological washing powders contain enzymes. Explain why the washing powders may become inefficient at high temperatures.

18 Pepsin is an enzyme found in the stomach. It breaks down proteins into amino acids. Draw a diagram to explain why pepsin cannot break down starch.

Diffusion

You will find out:

- about the movement of molecules
- about diffusion across cell membranes
- about factors that affect the rate of diffusion
- about diffusion in the body

What's that stink?

If someone lets off a stink bomb at one end of a corridor why does the whole corridor smell? Simple – it is called **diffusion**. The smelly gas molecules spread out through all the space available. Diffusion is very important in our bodies. It helps to move substances in and out of cells.

Moving substances in the body

To stay alive the body needs to move lots of different substances in and out of cells across the **cell membrane**.

- When we breathe in, **oxygen** moves from the **lungs** into the red blood cells. It then moves from the red blood cells into body tissue.

- **Carbon dioxide** moves from body tissue into the blood. Then it moves from the blood into the lungs.

- After eating, digested food molecules move from the **small intestine** into the blood. They then leave the blood and go into body tissue.

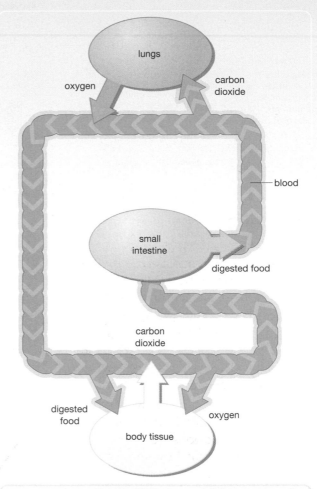

FIGURE 1: Substances move in and out of different parts of the body. What do substances have to pass across to get in and out of cells?

QUESTIONS

1. Which type of cell does oxygen enter from the lungs?
2. Which substances move from the small intestine into the blood?
3. Which substance moves from the blood into the lungs?
4. Name **two** substances that move into body tissue.

...alveoli ...carbon dioxide ...cell membrane ...concentration ...diffusion ...gas exchange

Watch Out High concentration – orange squash before you add the water.

Low concentration – orange squash with lots of water added.

What is diffusion?

> Diffusion is the movement of a substance from a region of high **concentration** to a region of low concentration.

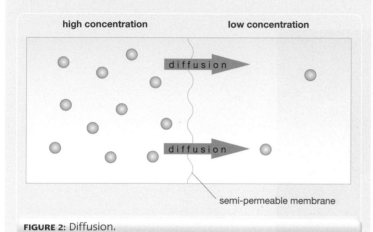

FIGURE 2: Diffusion.

Diffusion in the body

Molecules enter and leave cells because of diffusion. The direction molecules travel across the **semi-permeable** cell membrane depends on their concentration. When the concentration is higher inside a cell, the molecules pass out.

- **Alveoli** in the lungs have a higher concentration of oxygen than the blood that surrounds them. The oxygen diffuses into the blood. Carbon dioxide diffuses from the blood into the alveoli. Can you suggest a reason why? To maintain this **gas exchange**, breathing takes place.

- After eating there will be a high concentration of digested food molecules in the small intestine. This causes the small digested food molecules to diffuse through the cells of the small intestine wall into the blood.

QUESTIONS

5 When the concentration of oxygen is lower inside a cell than the blood around it, will oxygen move into or out of the cell?

6 How is a high concentration of oxygen maintained in the lungs?

7 Explain why fibre molecules do not diffuse through the small intestine wall.

Changing the rate of diffusion

When molecules in a liquid or a gas spread out they move in all directions. This is known as random movement of molecules. However, most of the molecules will move from a high concentration to a low concentration. Using these ideas, the definition of diffusion can be modified.

> Diffusion is the net movement of particles from an area of high concentration to an area of low concentration due to the random movement of individual particles.

The rate of diffusion can be increased by:

- increasing the **surface area**
- decreasing the diffusion distance
- a greater concentration difference.

Adapted for diffusion

Diffusion takes place in **villi** in the small intestine and alveoli in the lungs. Both have special adaptations to increase the rate of diffusion.

villus wall is only one cell thick; digested food does not have far to diffuse into the blood

a good blood supply means that the digested food is quickly taken away from the villus so more can diffuse across to replace it

the small intestine wall is covered in finger-like extensions called villi. The cells of the villi wall have folds in them called microvilli. The result is a surface area of approximately 9m²

the membrane of the villus is permeable to food molecules this is important as it means they can pass through the membrane

FIGURE 3: Diffusion of digested food molecules from a villus into the blood.

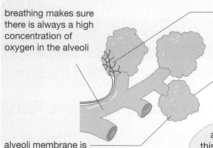

breathing makes sure there is always a high concentration of oxygen in the alveoli

a good blood supply makes sure that as soon as oxygen diffuses into the blood it is replaced with blood containing very little oxygen

the alveolus wall is only one cell thick so the gases do not have far to travel

there are large numbers of alveoli; this helps to increase the surface area, so more molecules can move across at any one time

alveoli membrane is permeable to gases and is also moist, which helps to speed up diffusion

FIGURE 4: Diffusion of oxygen from alveoli into the blood.

QUESTIONS

8 Explain why an increase in the surface area of the small intestine increases the rate of diffusion.

9 Explain how carbon dioxide is removed from the body. Include the following words in your answer.

diffusion   concentration   breathing

More on moving substances

Diffusion is important when it comes to moving substances into and out of whole organisms.

Keeping a foetus alive

A **foetus** growing inside the mother's **uterus** needs food and oxygen to stay alive. Food and oxygen pass from the mother's blood to the foetus's blood by diffusion.

The foetus makes carbon dioxide and other wastes. These wastes pass from the foetus into the mother's blood.

You will find out:

- how oxygen reaches a developing foetus
- how a foetus removes waste
- how substances in plants move in and out of the leaves

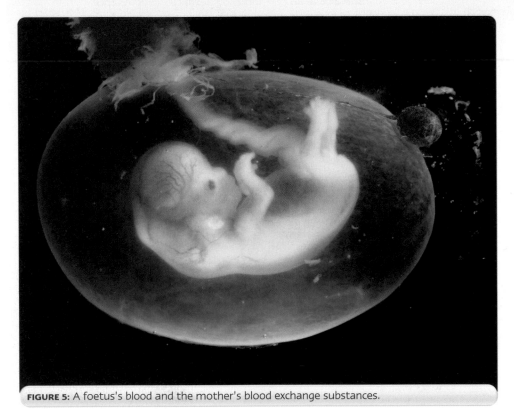

FIGURE 5: A foetus's blood and the mother's blood exchange substances.

Movement of substances in plant leaves

Plants use carbon dioxide for photosynthesis. They get carbon dioxide from the air by moving it in through the leaves. At the same time, oxygen moves out of the leaves.

Plants also lose water. This is lost by **evaporation** from the surface of the leaves.

Watch Out! Water gets into plants through the roots and leaves plants through the leaves. Water can't get in through the leaves.

▓ QUESTIONS ▓

10 Name **two** substances that move from a foetus into the mother's blood.

11 Name **two** substances that move from the mother's blood into a foetus.

12 Why do plants need carbon dioxide?

13 What substance do plants lose by evaporation from their leaves?

...air spaces ...evaporation ...foetus

Diffusion and the placenta

A foetus needs to be supplied with food and oxygen from its mother in order for it to develop. The mother's blood contains dissolved food such as glucose and amino acids.

The mother's blood and the blood of the foetus come close together in the **placenta**. However, the blood does not mix since mother and foetus often have different blood groups and mixing would be fatal. Dissolved food and oxygen pass into the foetus's blood and carbon dioxide and waste products pass out into the mother's blood by diffusion.

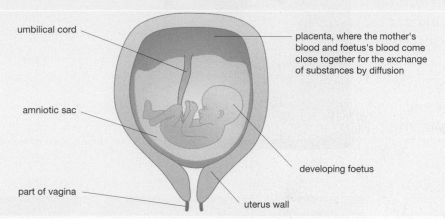

FIGURE 6: A foetus is attached to the placenta by the umbilical cord. Why should the foetus's blood and its mother's blood not mix?

Diffusion and the leaf

Plants use up carbon dioxide during photosynthesis. The concentration of carbon dioxide inside a leaf is therefore low during photosynthesis. The higher concentration of carbon dioxide in the air around the plant causes the gas to move into the leaf by diffusion. It diffuses through small pores called **stomata**. During photosynthesis, oxygen levels increase inside the leaf. This causes oxygen to diffuse out of the leaf into the air.

Inside a leaf there are lots of **air spaces**. Water vapour collects inside the air spaces, diffuses out of the leaf through the stomata and evaporates. More water, brought to the leaf in the xylem vessels from the roots, replaces the lost water.

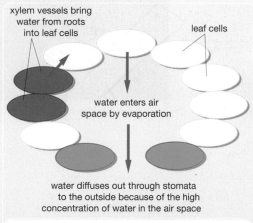

FIGURE 7: Movement of water in plants. How does water enter a plant?

```
QUESTIONS
```

14 By what process does oxygen move from the mother's blood into the blood of the foetus?

15 Explain why the placenta is so important to a developing foetus.

16 Describe how carbon dioxide moves into a leaf.

17 Explain why water diffuses out through the stomata.

Adapted for diffusion

The placenta

It is important to move substances across the placenta as quickly as possible. To speed up movement, the placenta has:

■ a very large surface area

■ a very thin wall so substances only have a short distance to diffuse.

The leaf

To increase the rate of gas exchange, the leaf has a large surface area. The under-surface of the leaf also has many stomata through which the gases can diffuse.

Synapses

A **synapse** is a gap between two neurones (nerve cells). To carry a signal from one neurone to the next, the synapse releases a transmitter substance. This is a special chemical that can diffuse across the gap between the two neurones. When it reaches the other side of the synapse, it causes an impulse to travel along the neurone.

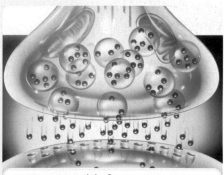

FIGURE 8: A model of a synapse.

```
QUESTIONS
```

18 During pregnancy, part of the placenta can break away from the uterus wall. Explain why this could harm the foetus.

19 Explain why there is less diffusion of gases through the upper surface of a leaf compared with the lower surface.

20 Transmitter substance is only made on one side of a synapse. Suggest **one** reason for this.

Keep it moving

You will find out:

- about blood cells and what they do
- about different types of blood vessels
- how blood vessels are adapted to their functions

Need a new heart? It's a pig!

In 1968 Dr Ross of the National Heart Hospital in London attempted to transplant a pig's heart into a patient. The heart was rejected by the patient's body.

Scientists have now cloned genetically-engineered pigs. They hope these pigs will provide new hearts for humans without the risk of rejection.

Is blood really red?

Blood looks like a red liquid. But if it is looked at through a microscope blood is very different. It is made of a yellow liquid called **plasma**. Blood looks red because it contains tiny **red blood cells**. These cells transport oxygen around the body. There are also **white blood cells** in blood. White blood cells help to defend the body against disease. Blood also contains tiny cell fragments called **platelets**. Platelets help to clot the blood if we cut ourselves.

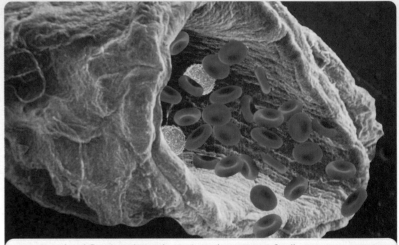

FIGURE 1: Blood flowing through a vein. What types of cells can you see?

Blood vessels

Blood is carried around the body in three different types of blood vessels:

- **artery**
- **vein**
- **capillary**.

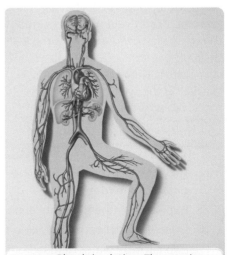

FIGURE 2: Blood circulation. The arteries are shown in red and the veins in blue.

QUESTIONS

1. Match up each part of the blood to the job it does.

Part of the blood	Job
red blood cell	defends against disease
white blood cell	helps blood to clot
platelet	transports oxygen

2. Name **three** types of blood vessels.

...artery ...capillary ...haemoglobin ...lumen ...oxyhaemoglobin ...plasma

Doing their job

Blood has many important functions. Each part of the blood is adapted to carry out its function.

Red blood cells

Red blood cells are adapted to carry as much oxygen as possible.

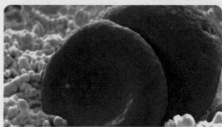

FIGURE 3: Red blood cells. Why are they disc-shaped?

- Their red colour comes from a chemical called **haemoglobin**. Oxygen joins to haemoglobin, which allows it to be transported around the body.

- They do not have a nucleus. This leaves more room to carry oxygen.

- They are disc-shaped and have a dent on both sides. This helps them to absorb a lot of oxygen.

- They are very small so they can carry oxygen to all parts of the body.

White blood cells

White blood cells are adapted to change shape.

- They can wrap around microbes and engulf them.

- They can squeeze through capillary walls to reach microbes.

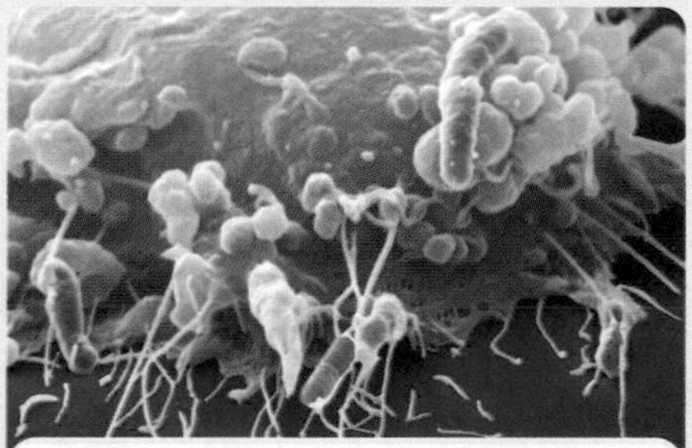

FIGURE 4: A white blood cell engulfing a virus. What are the advantages to a white blood cell of being able to change shape?

Plasma

Liquid plasma is adapted to transport dissolved substances such as water, hormones, antibodies and waste products around the body.

The transport vessels

- Arteries transport blood away from the heart.

- Veins transport blood to the heart.

- Capillaries join arteries to veins. Materials such as oxygen are exchanged between the capillaries and the body tissue.

QUESTIONS

3. Explain **one** way in which a red blood cell is adapted to its function.
4. Explain why white blood cells need to be able to change shape.
5. Why is plasma a liquid?
6. Which type of blood vessel transports blood away from the heart?

More on red blood cells

The shape of a red blood cell means it has a large surface area compared to its volume. This enables it to absorb a lot of oxygen.

Haemoglobin is a very special chemical. In the lungs it reacts with oxygen to form **oxyhaemoglobin**. When it reaches tissue it separates into haemoglobin and oxygen. The oxygen diffuses into the tissue cells and the red blood cells return to the lungs to pick up more oxygen.

Adaptation of blood vessels

Blood vessel	Structure	Adaptation
artery	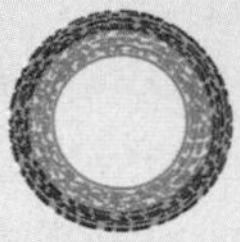	thick muscular and elastic wall to help it withstand high blood pressure as blood leaves the heart
vein	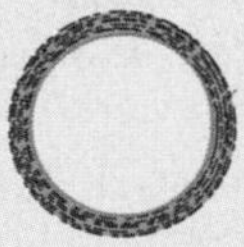	large **lumen** to help blood flow at low pressure; valves stop blood from flowing the wrong way
capillary		thin, permeable wall to allow exchange of material with body tissue

QUESTIONS

7. Why is oxyhaemoglobin such an important molecule and where does it form?
8. Explain the differences between veins and arteries relative to their functions.
9. Why are the walls of capillaries permeable?

What does the heart do?

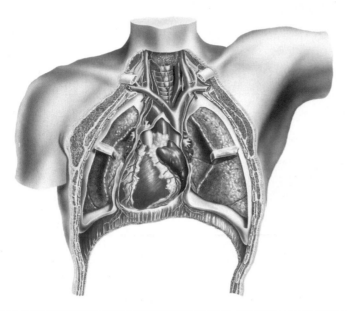

FIGURE 5: The heart and lungs. The red-coloured vessels carry blood away from the heart to the rest of the body. The blue-coloured vessels carry blood back to the heart.

The heart pumps blood around the body. There are two sides to a heart.

- The right side pumps blood to the lungs.
- The left side pumps blood to the rest of the body.
- The blood leaves the heart in arteries where the **pressure** is high.
- The blood returns to the heart at low pressure in veins.

Heart problems

Blood flows through arteries at high pressure. Saturated animal fats such as **cholesterol** can stick to the walls of arteries. This can slow down or block the flow of blood. If this happens in a main blood vessel it can cause a heart attack or a stroke.

Mending the heart

The heart or parts of the heart can be replaced either mechanically or biologically.

- Mechanically. Sometimes the heart valves do not work properly or they wear out. Special mechanical valves are used as replacements.
- Biologically. If the heart breaks down completely, a heart **transplant** is needed.

FIGURE 6: A mechanical heart or valves can be used to replace a damaged heart.

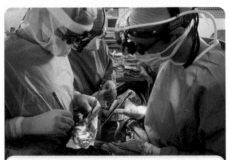

FIGURE 7: A patient has a heart transplant if their own heart has failed.

QUESTIONS

10 Which side of the heart pumps blood to the lungs?

11 Which side of the heart pumps blood to the rest of the body?

12 Which substance can slow down the flow of blood in arteries?

13 Describe how the heart can be mended mechanically.

...atrium ...chamber ...cholesterol ...coronary artery ...double circulatory system

Structure and function of the heart

There are four parts to the heart called **chambers**.

- Two **atria** receive blood from veins.
- Two **ventricles** pump blood into arteries.

There are also **valves** in the heart. They prevent the blood flowing backwards when the heart relaxes and so maintain blood pressure.

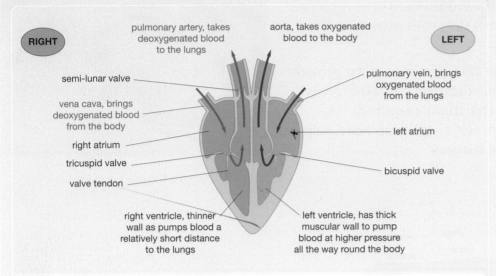

FIGURE 8: Blood flow in the heart. Which blood vessel brings blood to the heart from the body?

Treating heart disease

Coronary arteries supply the heart with food and oxygen. Too much cholesterol in the diet can lead to the blockage of a coronary artery. This can cause serious heart problems and even the need for a heart transplant. There are problems with heart operations.

- In heart transplants the donor heart needs to be a close match in size, age and tissue type. As the supply of donor hearts is limited and irregular, the chances of getting a suitable heart are low. After a transplant there is a possibility of **rejection** and the patient must take drugs to stop their immune system attacking their new heart.
- Mechanical replacement valves are very small and difficult to fit. **Pacemakers** can be attached to the heart to help it beat. However, they need internal batteries that have to be replaced. There is also a chance of rejection.

QUESTIONS

14 List the structures blood passes through as it travels from the vena cava to the aorta.

15 Explain why the left ventricle has a thicker muscle wall than the right ventricle.

16 Name **three** different valves found in the heart and describe the function of each.

17 Write a letter to someone explaining why it is important to watch how much cholesterol is in their diet. Include the problems they might face if their heart stops working.

Double circulation

Humans have a **double circulatory system** of arteries, veins and capillaries.

- One circuit links the heart and lungs.
- One circuit links the heart and the body.

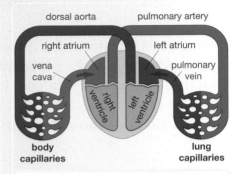

FIGURE 9: Double circulatory system. In which circuit does the blood travel furthest?

The heart is made up of two pumps. The advantage of this is that blood going to the body can be pumped at a much higher pressure than blood going to the lungs. This provides a greater rate of flow to all the body tissue.

Cholesterol build-up

Sometimes cholesterol in the blood sticks to the inside of artery walls. As it builds up it forms a plaque that restricts the flow of blood. Some of this cholesterol can break away and block the artery completely.

QUESTIONS

18 Suggest **two** ways to reduce cholesterol in the blood.

19 Some babies are born with a hole between the two ventricles in their heart. Suggest why their muscles would receive less oxygen.

20 Read the section on treating heart disease. Describe the advantages and disadvantages of a pacemaker and heart valves over a heart transplant.

Divide and rule

You will find out:

- why cells divide
- about advantages of being multi-cellular
- how cells divide by mitosis

Did you 'ear the one about the mouse?

Did you know it is possible to grow human tissue outside the body? Burns victims can now have their damaged skin repaired using sheets of new skin formed from skin cells grown in the laboratory.

Using a plastic framework under the skin of a mouse to provide a growing frame and a blood supply, scientists can also 'grow' human cartilage and skin cells into the shape required. The ability to grow something that looks like an ear can now help accident victims who need cosmetic surgery.

Making new cells

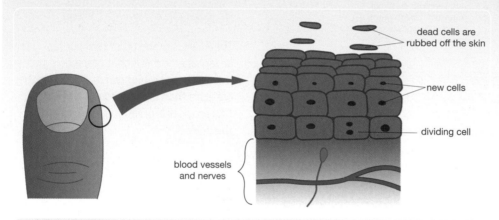

dead cells are rubbed off the skin

new cells

dividing cell

blood vessels and nerves

FIGURE 1: Skin cells dividing to make new skin.

Every day thousands of skin cells are lost from the skin. They are continuously rubbed off. All of these cells need to be replaced. To make new cells the body carries out **cell division**. Cells divide whenever the body needs to:

- grow
- replace worn out cells
- repair damaged tissue.

DID YOU KNOW?

By the time you are 20 you will have replaced all your skin cells 200 times!

■■ QUESTIONS ■■

1 How does the body replace lost skin cells?

2 Write down **three** reasons why the body needs to make new cells.

...cell division ...differentiation ...diploid ...genetically identical

The more cells the better

Amoeba is a **unicellular** organism. Its whole body is a single cell. It is microscopic in size. To grow larger than an amoeba an organism has to become **multi-cellular**.

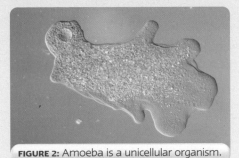

FIGURE 2: Amoeba is a unicellular organism.

Humans are multi-cellular. This gives them many advantages.

- Multi-cellular organisms can grow large.
- Cell **differentiation** takes place. Cells become different shapes or sizes to carry out specialised jobs.
- Organisms become more complex. Multi-cellular organisms can develop different organ systems. All the systems work together to make up the organism.

Dividing cells

Inside the nucleus of a human body cell there are 46 chromosomes. They are all different shapes and sizes. Each chromosome can be matched up with another of the same size. Humans have 23 pairs of chromosomes. The chromosomes in a pair look the same and carry similar information. They are called **homologous** pairs. When a cell has pairs of chromosomes it is called a **diploid** cell.

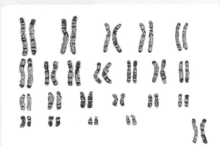

FIGURE 3: Twenty-three homologous pairs of chromosomes from a human cell. How many single chromosomes are there in a human cell?

During growth a type of cell division called **mitosis** makes new cells. The new cells are exact copies and contain 23 pairs of chromosomes.

QUESTIONS

3   Suggest **one** advantage of being multi-cellular.
4   Which type of human cell does **not** have chromosomes?
5   a   Explain what is meant by the term diploid.
    b   How many pairs of chromosomes are there in a diploid human body cell?

Size matters

The size that a single cell can grow to is limited by its surface area to volume ratio.

1 cm x 1 cm x 1 cm
surface area = 6 cm²
volume = 1 cm³
ratio = **6 : 1**

3 cm x 3 cm x 3 cm
surface area = 54 cm²
volume = 27 cm³
ratio = 54 : 27 = **2 : 1**

FIGURE 4: Surface area to volume ratios in two cubes. Why can cells not grow too large?

The larger cube has a much smaller surface area compared to its volume. A cell this size could not absorb enough food and oxygen through the surface of its membrane to stay alive. This is why large multi-cellular organisms have developed transport systems. Human body cells receive enough oxygen because blood transports oxygen round the body.

Mitosis and chromosomes

During mitosis, **genetically identical** cells are made. Each new cell contains identical chromosomes to the original cell.

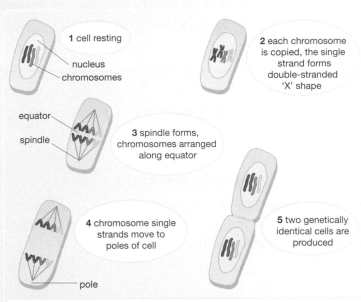

1 cell resting
nucleus
chromosomes

2 each chromosome is copied, the single strand forms double-stranded 'X' shape

equator
spindle

3 spindle forms, chromosomes arranged along equator

4 chromosome single strands move to poles of cell

5 two genetically identical cells are produced

pole

FIGURE 5: Mitosis. At what stage in mitosis are chromosomes copied?

QUESTIONS

6   Does an elephant or a mouse have a smaller surface area to volume ratio?
7   Suggest why a large surface area to volume ratio is an advantage to an amoeba.
8   Describe the stages involved when the body makes a new layer of skin.

Sunny-side up!

Mohammed likes eating an **egg** for breakfast. He knows a hen's egg has a hard outer shell for protection. Cracking open the egg, Mohammed finds the albumen (white) and the yolk (yellow). The hen's egg has not been fertilised by **sperm** from a male so cannot develop into an **embryo**.

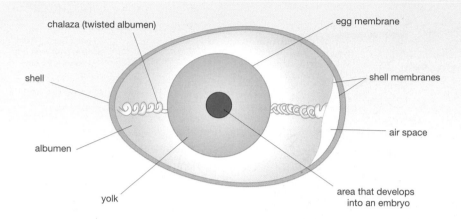

chalaza (twisted albumen)

egg membrane

shell

shell membranes

air space

albumen

yolk

area that develops into an embryo

FIGURE 6: A hen's egg. What needs to happen for the egg to develop into an embryo?

Human eggs and sperm

Eggs and sperm are called sex cells or reproductive **gametes**. Gametes join during **fertilisation**. Eggs and sperm are specially adapted to do their jobs.

Egg

- An egg is much larger than a sperm because it contains food for the developing embryo.
- The nucleus of an egg contains genes which are the instructions to make new cells.

Sperm

- A sperm is much smaller than an egg.
- It has a tail to help it move.
- A male releases millions of sperm to increase the chance of one reaching an egg.
- The nucleus of a sperm contains genes which are the instructions to make new cells.

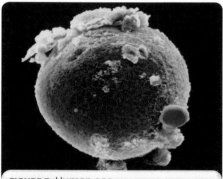

FIGURE 7: Human egg.

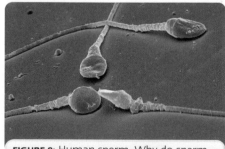

FIGURE 8: Human sperm. Why do sperm have a tail?

QUESTIONS

9 What is another name for a male gamete?

10 What is it called when a sperm and an egg join?

11 Describe how a sperm is adapted to do its job.

12 Describe how an egg is adapted to do its job.

...acrosome ...diploid number ...egg ...embryo ...fertilisation ...gamete

Making gametes

Human body cells have 23 pairs of chromosomes. This full set of chromosomes is called the **diploid number**. The gametes (egg and sperm) contain only one chromosome from each pair. So gametes have half a set of chromosomes, called the **haploid number**. During fertilisation the gametes join to form a **zygote**. The zygote is diploid and can develop into an embryo.

Meiosis is a special type of cell division that produces gametes. When fertilisationtakes place gametes from a male and female join. The resulting offspring have genes from both parents. This makes them different to their parents. They are new individuals. Reproduction using meiosis results in a lot of genetic **variation** within a species. Animals such as amoeba use mitosis for reproduction so all their offspring are genetically identical.

 Body cells are diploid. Gametes are haploid. They only have half the number of chromosomes.

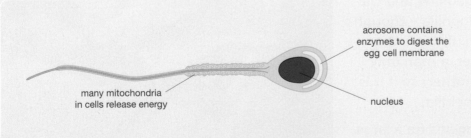

FIGURE 9: What process during sexual reproduction introduces genetic variation?

Moving sperm

Sperm have to travel a long way and then get inside an egg. They are specially adapted to do this.

- A sperm has large numbers of mitochondria to release energy for motion.
- A structure called an **acrosome** on the sperm head releases enzymes that digest the cell membrane of an egg allowing the sperm inside.

acrosome contains enzymes to digest the egg cell membrane

many mitochondria in cells release energy

nucleus

FIGURE 10: A sperm. Why are there a lot of mitochondria in some of its cells?

QUESTIONS

13 Where in the human body does meiosis take place?

14 If sperm and eggs were diploid how many chromosomes would the human zygote have?

15 Explain the function of the following parts of a sperm cell:
   a mitochondria
   b acrosome.

Meiosis and chromosomes

Gametes are made when diploid cells divide by meiosis to produce haploid cells. Meiosis involves two divisions:

- first the pairs of chromosomes separate
- then the chromosomes divide in the same way as in mitosis.

1 homologous chromosomes pair up

 pole

2 one from each pair moves to opposite poles

3 strands of chromosomes move to opposite poles

4 four new haploid cells form

FIGURE 11: Meiosis. At what stage do chromosome pairs move to the poles of the cell?

Your body cells divide by mitosis. When making eggs or sperm, cells divide by meiosis.

QUESTIONS

16 Describe the stages involved when sperm is made inside the testes.

17 Describe **two** ways in which meiosis is different to mitosis.

Genetic disorders in the Royal Family

SELF-CHECK ACTIVITY

STEP 1

One of the problems with tracing haemophilia through a family line is that it is not always clear which of the offspring are carriers. Why is this?

CONTEXT

Imagine what would happen if, when you cut yourself, the wound did not heal. This condition is called haemophilia and it is a disorder of the blood. A person suffering from haemophilia lacks a clotting agent in their blood. If they are cut their wounds continue to bleed; there can be bleeding inside the body and their body bruises more easily.

Haemophilia is an inherited condition; it is not contagious which means it cannot be caught by being near someone who has it.

Haemophilia is a condition that is sex-linked – it can only be carried on an X chromosome. A woman has two X chromosomes. A man has one X chromosome and one Y chromosome. Haemophilia is a recessive characteristic, which means that if a woman has inherited a 'healthy' X chromosome from one parent and a 'damaged' (i.e. haemophilia) chromosome from the other parent, the healthy chromosome dominates the damaged one and the woman does not suffer from haemophilia – though she does carry it and may pass it on. If this is the case she is called a 'carrier'. However, a man only has one X chromosome (from his mother) so if it is damaged he will suffer from haemophilia.

Queen Victoria, who was queen of England for a large part of the 19th Century, was a carrier of haemophilia. She did not suffer from the disease herself but she passed on the affected chromosome to some of her nine children. Sons who inherited the affected chromosome suffered from haemophilia (Prince Leopold died at the age of 31) and daughters who inherited the affected chromosome carried it on to the next generation. Two of Victoria's grandsons suffered from haemophilia and seven of her great grandsons.

STEP 2

It is not always clear whether offspring are sufferers either. Suggest why this might be so.

If a woman who is a carrier has a child by a man who does not have haemophilia, what are the chances of the condition being passed on to:
a a daughter **b** a son?

Why is it impossible for a man to be a carrier of haemophilia?

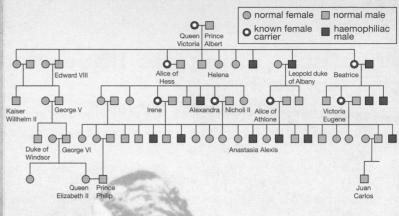

○ normal female	▢ normal male
◎ known female carrier	▪ haemophiliac male

Queen Victoria's family tree showing four generations.

Labels: Queen Victoria, Prince Albert, Edward VIII, Alice of Hess, Helena, Leopold duke of Albany, Beatrice, Kaiser Willhelm II, George V, Irene, Alexandra, Nicholi II, Alice of Athlone, Victoria Eugene, Duke of Windsor, George VI, Anastasia Alexis, Juan Carlos, Queen Elizabeth II, Prince Philip

Maximise your grade

These sentences show what you need to be including in your work. Use these to improve your work and to be successful.

Grade	Answer includes...
F	Know that haemophilia is an inherited condition.
	Know that some genetic characteristics, such as red hair, can be seen and that other characteristics, such as haemophilia, cannot be seen.
	Know that a carrier does not suffer from haemophilia, their life is normal.
	Know that a carrier does not show any symptoms of the condition.
C	Understand that a daughter will have a 50/50 chance of being a carrier, and that a son will have a 50/50 chance of being a haemophiliac.
	Explain with reference to chromosomes why the condition in males will always be expressed rather than being a carrier.
A	Explain with reference to chromosomes why a female can be a carrier or a haemophiliac.
	Explain with reference to chromosomes why a female haemophiliac could be produced from a female carrier and a male haemophiliac.

It is extremely unlikely that a woman would suffer from haemophilia. What would have to be true about her parents for this to stand a chance of happening?

Growing up

You will find out:

- about plant cells
- how animals and plants grow
- how cells can change as they grow
- about stem cells

Who said chickens haven't got the nerve?

If a person damages their nerve cells their body cannot make new ones. However, scientists have found a way to grow human nerve cells in chickens.

They have taken **stem cells** from human bone marrow and put them into chicken embryos. Stem cells are special cells that have the ability to form different cells. Normally stem cells from bone marrow turn into blood cells. Scientists have found that these stem cells can be turned into nerve cells in chicken embryos.

However, scientists are still a long way off using this to replace damaged nerve cells in the human body.

Plant cells

A plant cell has the following parts.

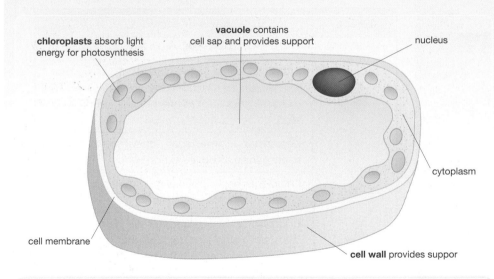

chloroplasts absorb light energy for photosynthesis

vacuole contains cell sap and provides support

nucleus

cytoplasm

cell membrane

cell wall provides suppor

FIGURE 1: A plant cell.

Changing cells

For a fertilised egg to grow into an embryo and a foetus, the cells need to divide and change. The cells change so they can carry out different jobs. Some cells turn into nerve cells. Others change into bone cells. This change is called **cell differentiation**.

QUESTIONS

1 Match up each part of a cell with the job it does.

Part of cell	Job
vacuole	absorb light energy for photosynthesis
cell wall	contains cell sap and provides support
chloroplast	provides support

2 What happens to a cell during cell differentiation?

...*cell differentiation* ...*cell wall* ...*chloroplast* ...*elongate*

Similar but different

Both animal and plant cells have a nucleus, cytoplasm and a cell membrane. This makes them similar. However there are ways in which they are very different as shown in the table.

Plant cell	Animal cell
cellulose cell wall for support	no cell wall
most have chloroplasts for photosynthesis	no chloroplasts
large vacuole containing cell sap	may have a small vacuole but no cell sap

Animal and plant growth

Animals and plants grow in different ways. Animals tend to grow to a certain size and then stop. Plants can continue to grow.

DID YOU KNOW?

Blue whales grow very fast. A calf can have a mass of 26 tonnes before it is a year old. That is about the weight of two double-decker buses!

FIGURE 2: **a** Animal growth is limited. If this stick insect grew too much it would be crushed by the weight of its skeleton. **b** Plants continue to grow.

Stem cells

A few days after an egg is fertilised it contains a group of cells called stem cells. These all have the same simple cell structure. They divide and then differentiate to form all the different specialised cells in the body. As the embryo grows all the specialised cells form **tissues** and **organs**.

Some stem cells are found in the adult body. Bone marrow contains stem cells that turn into different types of blood cells.

QUESTIONS

3 Name **three** structures found in a plant cell but not in an animal cell.

4 Name **three** structures found in both an animal cell and a plant cell.

5 Describe how animal growth is different to plant growth.

6 What is a cell called before it becomes specialised?

WANT TO KNOW MORE?

You can find out more about stem cells from:

http://gslc.genetics.utah.edu/units/stemcells/whatissc/

Animal cell and plant cell growth

The cells of animals and plants cause them to grow in different ways.

Plant	Animal
most growth is due to cells **elongating** (growing longer), not dividing	growth is due to cells dividing
cell division only normally occurs at the tips of shoots and roots	cell division occurs all over the body
many cells never lose the ability to differentiate	most animal cells lose the ability to differentiate very early on

Stem cell research

Scientists have found ways of making stem cells develop into other specialised cells in the hope of replacing damaged cells.

However, many people object to stem cell research because it can involve human embryos. Scientists use embryo stem cells because they are easier to grow than adult stem cells.

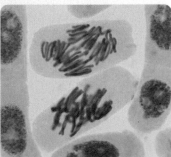

FIGURE 3: Cell division in the tip of a root of a germinating plant.

QUESTIONS

7 Describe how growth in a finger is different to growth in a root.

8 Which type of cell division occurs in a root tip?

9 Should scientists be allowed to use embryo stem cells? Give **one** reason for your answer.

Human growth

There are five main stages in human growth.

You will find out:
- about the stages in human growth
- about gestation
- about problems in human growth

1 infancy

2 childhood

3 adolescence (puberty)

4 adulthood (maturity)

5 old age

QUESTIONS

10 Without looking at the book, write down the **five** main stages in human growth in the correct order.

11 Which stage of human growth do you think you are in?

...adolescence ...adulthood ...childhood ...gestation

Gestation

Gestation is the length of time from fertilisation to birth. The larger the animal the longer gestation tends to be. This is because the animal needs time to develop enough to survive outside the uterus. An elephant has a gestation of 700 days and a rat has a gestation of 22 days!

Growth of a baby

Different parts of the foetus and baby grow at different rates. The brain and head develop quickly to coordinate the complex human structure and chemical activity.

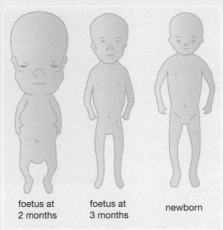

foetus at 2 months   foetus at 3 months   newborn

FIGURE 4: Human growth.

Growth curves

After a baby is born it has regular growth checks. The baby's weight and head size are recorded. These measurements show if the baby is growing at a normal rate.

Age in months	0	3	6	9	12	15	18	21	24	27	30
Weight in kg	2.5	5.0	6.4	7.5	8.8	9.6	9.8	10.0	10.1	10.4	10.7
Head size in cm	36.0	41.2	43.6	45.2	46.4	47.2	47.8	48.2	48.6	49.0	49.2

QUESTIONS

12 Explain why the gestation period of an elephant is longer than that of a rat.

13 Which parts of a foetus grow the quickest?

14 **a** Plot the data from the table above on to a graph.

   b During which period is the rate of growth fastest?

15 Use this graph of human growth to answer the questions.

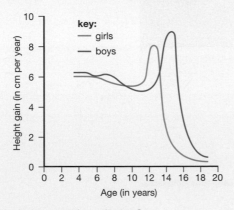

a At what age do boys reach puberty? Explain your answer.

b Describe the change in the graph when girls reach adulthood at 18.

c Suggest what might happen to the height of adults as they reach old age.

Growth problems

Measuring the weight and head size of a baby is very important. The results can be plotted on a graph and compared with graphs showing expected growth.

- Poor weight gain can indicate problems with a baby's digestive system.
- Larger than normal head size can indicate fluid collection on the brain or the separate skull bones not fusing together.

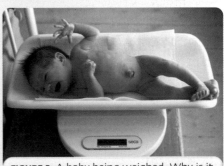

FIGURE 5: A baby being weighed. Why is it important to record a baby's development?

QUESTIONS

16 How would problems in a baby's digestive system show up on a growth chart?

17 When the head of a baby was measured it was shown to be larger than expected. Suggest **one** problem the baby may have.

18 Suggest **one** reason why skull bones not fusing could be a problem to a baby.

Controlling plant growth

You will find out:
- about plant hormones
- how plants respond to light and gravity

Banana power

At the end of the summer many gardeners are faced with handfuls of unripe green tomatoes. Most gardeners either throw them away or make tomato chutney.

The alternative is to put the tomatoes in a bag with a ripe banana. Over-ripe bananas release a hormone that ripens fruit.

Plant hormones

Plants make special chemicals called **hormones**. Hormones control different processes in a plant:

- growth of shoots towards light
- growth of roots downwards into the soil, in response to **gravity**
- growth of flowers
- ripening of fruit.

FIGURE 1: a Shoots grow towards a light source and **b** roots grow downwards in response to gravity.

▪▪ QUESTIONS ▪▪

1 What name is given to chemicals inside plants that control growth?
2 Do plant shoots grow towards or away from light?
3 Which part of the plant responds to the force of gravity by growing downwards?
4 How does a hormone from a banana affect a green tomato?

...auxin ...elongate ...geotropism ...gravity ...hormone ...negative

Positive and negative

A plant is **sensitive**. It responds to different **stimuli**. A plant's response can be:

- **negative** – it grows away from a stimulus
- **positive** – it grows towards a stimulus.

A hormone called **auxin** controls the response. Auxin is made in the tips of roots and shoots of a plant. It travels through a plant in **solution**. The roots and shoots respond to auxin in different ways.

Phototropism

When a plant responds to light it is called **phototropism**.

- Plant shoots grow towards light. This response is called positive phototropism.
- Plant roots grow away from light. This is negative phototropism.

Geotropism

When a plant responds to gravity it is called **geotropism**.

- Plant shoots grow away from the pull of gravity. This response is called negative geotropism.
- Plant roots grow with the pull of gravity. This is positive geotropism.

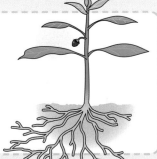

- Shoots are positively phototropic and negatively geotropic.
- Roots are negatively phototropic and positively geotropic.

 The 'positive' and 'negative' terms are difficult to remember.

If it's positive it grows towards the stimulus. Imagine being positively attracted to someone!

QUESTIONS

5   Name **two** responses in plants that involve auxin.

6   Explain **one** advantage of a plant shoot growing towards light.

7   Explain **one** advantage of a plant root growing down into soil.

8   Describe a simple experiment to show that cress seeds are positively phototropic.

How auxin works

When the tip of a shoot is cut off it stops growing. If the tip is replaced on the stem it starts to grow again. Removing the tip removes the source of auxin and stops growth.

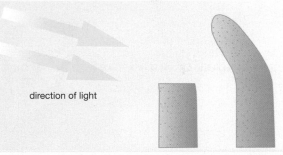

FIGURE 2: Growth of plant shoot tips in response to a light source. Why is only one shoot growing towards the light?

- Auxin is made in the tip.
- Auxin moves away from light and collects on the shady side of a shoot.
- Auxin causes cells on the shady side to **elongate** (grow longer) more than cells on the light side.
- The shady side becomes longer and causes the shoot to bend.

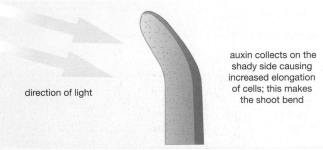

auxin collects on the shady side causing increased elongation of cells; this makes the shoot bend

direction of light

FIGURE 3: The mechanism of a plant shoot's positive response to a light source.

QUESTIONS

9   Look at the experiment shown in the diagram.

light all around

untreated seedling

substance **X**

treated seedling

seedlings at start   after 2 days

a   Describe the results of the experiment after 2 days.

b   Name substance **X**.

c   Explain the effect of substance **X** on the shoot.

Speeding up growth

Farmers can spray their crops with hormones to make the plants grow fruit.

FIGURE 4: Apples on a tree. What do farmers spray on trees to make fruit grow?

Slowing down growth

Farmers can also use hormones to slow down growth. This stops the fruit from falling off the tree before the harvest.

DID YOU KNOW?

Apple seeds contain a small quantity of cyanide that makes them taste bitter.

FIGURE 5: How do farmers stop fruit from falling off trees?

▥ QUESTIONS ▥

10 Copy and complete the following sentence.

Farmers can use h_____ to speed up or slow down plant g_____.

11 Suggest why farmers need to slow down the growth of fruit on their trees.

...dormant ...ethene ...germination ...gibberellic acid

Using plant hormones

Farmers, gardeners and fruit growers all find a use for plant hormones. They mostly use a man-made auxin called **synthetic auxin**.

Selective weedkillers

Synthetic auxin is sprayed on crops to kill weeds. The hormone makes weeds grow too fast and they die. The concentration used only affects broad-leaved weeds. The narrow-leaved crops are unaffected. Because they only kill certain weeds they are called **selective weedkillers**.

FIGURE 6: A farmer spraying a cereal crop with a selective weedkiller. Why is the weedkiller described as 'selective'?

Growing roots

New plants can be grown by taking cuttings from existing plants. A cutting is dipped into a hormone-based **rooting powder**. The synthetic auxin in the powder stimulates roots to grow from the shoot.

Seedless grapes

Fruits only grow on plants after the flower has been fertilised. Some growers spray unfertilised plants with synthetic auxin. This causes the fruits to grow without the flowers being fertilised. This means the fruits have no pips, such as seedless grapes.

Transporting bananas

Bananas are easily damaged during transport. To avoid this they are harvested before they are ripe. During transport a hormone called **ethene** is sprayed on them. Ethene causes bananas to ripen ready for sale.

Sleeping seeds

The ginseng plant is grown because people believe its roots can help the body fight disease. To grow the plant from seed takes many years. The seeds taken from a parent plant are **dormant**. This means they are inactive and **germination** will not take place until the conditions are right. Ginseng seeds have to be kept cold for a year before they break their dormancy. Growers have found they can use a hormone called **gibberellic acid** to force germination of the seeds without cold. The growers get their plants a year earlier which helps them make more money.

FIGURE 7: How are bananas supplied undamaged and ripe to supermarkets?

QUESTIONS

12 How do hormones kill weeds?

13 Describe how a farmer can produce grapes without seeds.

14 One reason bananas are picked before they are ripe is to prevent damage. Suggest another reason.

15 Suggest **one** reason why some people prefer fruit that has not been sprayed with hormones.

New genes for old

You will find out:
- how plants and animals can be changed by selective breeding
- about advantages and disadvantages of selective breeding
- how mutations happen

An apple a day could stop tooth decay

One day tooth decay may be prevented by eating apples. Scientists have identified a protein that stops tooth-rotting bacteria sticking to teeth. They hope to place the gene that codes for the protein into apples. The apple would then make the protein and eating an apple would stop the bacteria sticking to your teeth!

Selecting the best

Farmers are always trying to make their animals and plants produce more. They choose animals and plants with the **characteristics** they want. Then they **breed** them to produce **offspring** that have the characteristics.

Lettuces last longer.

Chickens lay more eggs.

Cows produce more milk.

Plants and animals can also change by a process called **mutation**. A mutation happens when there is a change in an animal's or plant's genes.

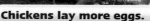

QUESTIONS

1. Why do farmers want to plant wheat crops that grow quickly?
2. Why do farmers want pigs that produce a lot of baby pigs?
3. Name **one** characteristic of strawberry plants that is useful to gardeners.

...base sequence ...breed ...characteristic ...cross-breed ...gene pool ...inbred

Designing a better cow

FIGURE 1: Jersey cows (left) produce small amounts of very creamy milk and Friesian cows (right) produce large amounts of slightly creamy milk.

To breed a cow that has a high **yield** (quantity) of creamy milk farmers carry out a **selective breeding** programme.

■ Choose a Jersey cow that produces the creamiest milk.

■ Choose a Friesian cow with the highest milk yield.

■ **Cross-breed** these cows by mating a Friesian cow with a Jersey bull and a Jersey cow with a Friesian bull.

■ Select the best cross-breeds, i.e. the offspring that produce large quantities of creamy milk.

■ Repeat the selection and breeding process for a number of generations.

Mutation

Change can also happen by mutation. A gene change usually causes harm to the organism. Haemophilia is a condition in humans where the blood does not clot properly and it can be caused by a mutation.

Some mutations can be an advantage to an organism giving it a better chance of survival. For example, bacteria can mutate and become resistant to antibiotics.

Mutations can be caused by:

■ radiation such as X-rays

■ chemicals such as those found in cigarette smoke

■ chance.

DID YOU KNOW?

Down's syndrome is caused by a mutation. The person has an extra chromosome.

QUESTIONS

4 Describe how a farmer could produce a plant with large sweet strawberries if she starts with a plant that has small sweet berries and one with large non-sweet berries.

5 Describe **one** example of a mutation that is an advantage to an organism.

6 Name **two** things that can cause mutations.

Problems with a 'designer animal'

Selective breeding often involves animals that are closely related. This is called **inbreeding**. Inbreeding causes a reduction in the **gene pool** (the different genes available in a species). With a smaller gene pool there is less **variation**. For example, cows could lose genes that could help them survive a new disease.

Some animals are bred to show in competitions. The more an animal is selectively bred, the more chance there is of harmful recessive genes being expressed.

FIGURE 2: Bulldogs have been bred with large folds of skin on their faces. This is a recessive characteristic that reduces the chances of the dogs surviving in the wild because of problems with their sight.

The problem with mutations

When a gene mutates the DNA **base sequence** is changed. Spot the change in the sequence of DNA.

original base code	mutation
CACTTGGTCAAA	**CACTTGTCAAA**

A change in the sequence changes the protein that is made or even prevents its production.

Look at the messages.

Bring thermos on outing.	Bring mothers on outing.

'Thermos' and 'mothers' have the same letters but in a different order. The messages have different meanings!

It is the same with the base sequence. Cystic fibrosis is the result of a mutation in DNA. Sufferers have breathing problems caused by a change in the base sequence so that a different protein is made.

QUESTIONS

7 Why is variation in organisms important?

8 Suggest why a change in the DNA sequence could be a problem.

More of the same

You will find out:
- about asexual reproduction
- how cloning produces genetically identical copies
- how cows can be cloned
- how cloning was used to make Dolly the sheep

Meet 'Snuppy' the cloned puppy

Dolly the sheep was the first animal to be cloned from an adult. Now the world's first cloned dog has been created. He is an Afghan hound called Snuppy. Some pet owners hope that the technique can be used to clone dead pets but scientists stress their research is for medical purposes.

Making copies

The process of **cloning** is used to make copies of animals and plants. The copies are called **clones**. Clones are **genetically identical**. They all have the same DNA as the original animal or plant.

Cloning involves only one parent. It is an example of **asexual reproduction**.

Natural clones

Clones are genetically identical organisms. Sometimes clones are produced naturally. Human twins can be genetically identical. They are called **natural clones**.

FIGURE 1: Identical twins (left) are natural clones as they have the same DNA. Non-identical twins (right) are not clones as they have different DNA.

▪ QUESTIONS ▪

1. Why is cloning an example of asexual reproduction?
2. What was the first animal to be cloned from an adult?
3. What is special about the DNA of a clone and its parent?
4. Why are identical twins called natural clones?

...artificial insemination ...asexual reproduction ...clone ...cloning ...embryo transplantation

Cloning cows

If a farmer has a prize cow he will want to breed as many offspring as possible from it. A cow produces one calf a year so the farmer uses **surrogate** mothers to carry clones so that he gets more calves in a year. This is called **embryo transplantation**. Embryo calves are placed in surrogate mothers to develop in the normal way.

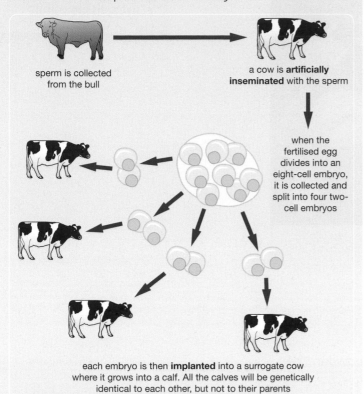

FIGURE 2: Embryo transplantation in cows. What is the term used to describe the placing of sperm from a bull inside a cow?

Importance of cloning

Cloning of animals has very important uses. Scientists are hoping to clone pigs to supply organs for transplants into humans.

Human embryos could also be cloned to provide **stem cells**. Stem cells could be transplanted into people suffering from diabetes so that they could make their own insulin. However, people are concerned that this would be unethical because the embryo is a living thing. Some people are also afraid that scientists will eventually be able to clone adult humans.

QUESTIONS

5   Describe the process of embryo transplantation.
6   Why do scientists hope to clone pigs?
7   Explain why some people are concerned about human cloning.

Cloning sheep

The clones from embryo transplants are clones of each other. However, because the original embryo formed from a fertilised egg they are not clones of the parents. The clones are a mixture of the two parents. Dolly the sheep was different. She was genetically identical to her single parent.

Dolly was cloned using the DNA in the nucleus of udder cells. The process is called **nuclear transfer**.

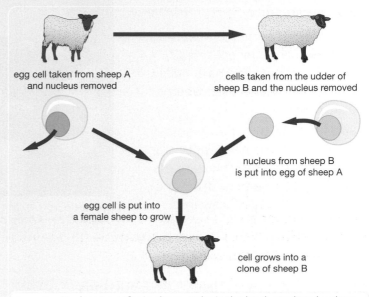

FIGURE 3: Nuclear transfer in sheep. Why is the lamb produced a clone of sheep B and not of sheep A?

Risks involved in cloning

- There is a low rate of success. There were 227 attempts to clone a sheep before Dolly was born.
- Research into human cloning raises many moral and ethical issues about creating life and then using it to help others.
- Dolly died of conditions linked to old age, yet she was only 7 years old. Her DNA may have already been old before she was born.

Benefits of cloning

- Cloned pigs could make up for a shortage in transplant organs and patients needing a transplant would not have to wait for someone to die.
- Diseases could be cured using embryonic stem cells.

QUESTIONS

8   Explain why Dolly was not related to the sheep that gave birth to her.
9   If you needed a new heart would you object to one from a cloned pig? Give **one** reason for your answer.
10 A friend objects to the use of embryonic stem cells. Write a short passage to persuade them they are wrong.

You will find out:

- how asexual reproduction takes place in plants
- about the advantages and disadvantages of cloned plants
- about plants cloned using tissue culture

Asexual reproduction in plants

Many plants reproduce by asexual reproduction. This process produces new plants very quickly. In asexual reproduction there is no fertilisation between male and female gametes. New plants are produced using **cell division** only. The new plants are clones of the parent plant.

- The part of the potato we eat is the **tuber**. Left long enough, it will grow shoots and roots from the 'eye' (bud).

- Strawberries grow stems called **runners**. The runners spread over the ground and have buds that grow into new strawberry plants.

- Spider plants grow new plants on their stems. The new plants are called **plantlets**. If the plantlets are cut off the parent plant and planted in soil they grow into adult plants.

FIGURE 4: How do potatoes reproduce? What is the process called?

New plants from old

Gardeners can clone plants by taking **cuttings**.

- A short stem is cut off the parent plant with a sharp knife.

- The end of the stem is dipped into plant hormone rooting powder. The hormone helps the plant to grow roots.

- The cutting is put into a pot containing sandy soil.

- A polythene bag is then put over the plant to keep the moisture in.

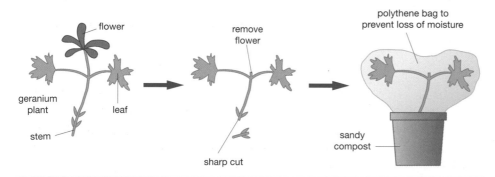

FIGURE 5: Taking a cutting. Suggest a reason why the cutting is put into sandy soil.

:: QUESTIONS ::

11 Describe how a strawberry plant reproduces asexually.

12 Describe how a new plant can be made from a cutting.

...aseptic technique ...cell division ...cutting

Why clone plants?

Advantages

- All the plants are genetically identical. All the cuttings taken from a red rose grow into red roses.
- Plants can take a long time to grow from seeds. Cloning produces lots of identical plants more quickly.
- Cloning enables growers to produce plants that are difficult to grow from seed such as bananas.

Disadvantages

- The plants are all genetically identical. If the environment changes or a new disease breaks out it is unlikely that any of the plants will survive.
- Cloning plants over many years has resulted in little genetic variation.

FIGURE 6: Gardeners are trying to grow old varieties to increase genetic variation in vegetables. Why is variation in a species beneficial?

QUESTIONS

13 Describe **one** advantage of cloning plants.
14 Describe **one** disadvantage of cloning plants.
15 Describe how you could produce five clones from a potato tuber.

Tissue culture

Small sections of plant tissue can be cloned using **tissue culture**. Tissue culture must be carried out using **aseptic technique** (everything has to be sterile).

- Plants with the desired characteristics are chosen.
- A large number of small pieces of tissue are taken from the parent plant.
- They are put into sterile test tubes that contain growth medium.
- The tissue pieces are left in suitable conditions to grow into plants.

FIGURE 7: Tissue culture. Suggest why it is important that aseptic technique is used.

Animal or plant clones?

Humans have been cloning plants for hundreds of years. Animals have only been cloned over the last few years. Why is this?

- Many plant cells retain the ability to differentiate into different cells. Root cells used in tissue culture have to change into all the different types of cells found in a plant.
- Most animal cells have lost the ability to differentiate.

QUESTIONS

16 Explain the term aseptic technique.
17 Suggest **two** suitable conditions needed for tissue cultures to grow into plants.
18 Explain why strawberry plants are easier to clone than sheep.

Module summary

Concept map

Animal and plant cells have the following parts: membrane, nucleus, cytoplasm, mitochondria.

Plant cells also have: cell wall, vacuole, chloroplasts.

Molecules of life
DNA is found in the nucleus of the cell. DNA carries coded information.

Chromosomes are made of DNA. A section of DNA is called a gene.

Enzymes are biological catalysts.

DNA fingerprints can be used to identify individuals.

The base sequence in DNA determines the order of amino acids in the protein.

Diffusion of substances takes place in the placenta.

In the lungs, oxygen diffuses into red blood cells. Carbon dioxide diffuses from the blood into the lungs.

Carbon dioxide and oxygen diffuse in and out of plants through the leaves.

Blood and diffusion

Blood is moved around the body in arteries, veins and capillaries. The heart pumps the blood.

Food diffuses from the small intestine into the blood.

After cells divide they become specialised. This is called differentiation. Undifferentiated cells are called stem cells.

Cell division and growth

Eggs and sperm are special cells called gametes. A type of cell division called meiosis produces them. Gametes contain the haploid number of chromosomes.

Cells divide by mitosis.

Plant hormones are chemicals that control the growth of shoots and roots, flowering and ripening of fruit.

Plant hormones

The hormone called auxin is involved in the plant's response to light (phototropism) and gravity (geotropism).

Cloning involves producing genetically identical copies.

Selective breeding involves breeding organisms with the best characteristics.

Using cells and DNA

Genetic engineering involves taking genes from one organism and putting them into another.

Module quiz

1   Which part of the cell contains DNA?

2   What does a gene code for?

3   What are proteins made of?

4   What is an enzyme?

5   Give **two** conditions that will denature an enzyme.

6   What is diffusion?

7   Name **one** place in the body where diffusion takes place.

8   How is the placenta adapted to increase the rate of diffusion?

9   Where would you find transmitter substance?

10 Name the **four** different parts of the blood and state their function.

11 What is the function of the heart?

12 Is a gamete haploid or diploid?

13 How is a sperm adapted to its function?

14 List the **five** stages of human growth.

15 Write down **two** commercial uses of plant hormones.

16 Explain why plant shoots are phototropic.

17 Why are clones identical?

18 Write down **one** advantage of selective breeding.

19 What is a gene mutation?

20 What do we call the process of taking DNA from one organism and putting it into another?

Literacy activity

The structure of DNA

James Watson and Frances Crick were the first scientists to build a model of DNA in 1953. They used ideas put forward by other scientists to work out the final structure. Maurice Wilkins and Rosalind Franklin had used X-ray crystallography to show that DNA was a helix. A chemist called Erwin Chargaff had shown the amounts of base A were equal to the amounts of base T and the amounts of base G equalled those of base C. Watson and Crick used this data to produce their model.

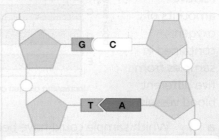

DNA model showing base A joined to base T and base C joined to base G.

QUESTIONS

1   Why are Watson and Crick so famous?

2   How did Rosalind Franklin contribute to the discovery of DNA structure?

3   Suggest why Watson and Crick joined base A to base T in their model.

All living things need energy. The Sun's energy is harnessed by green plants. The energy then flows through ecosystems. Bacteria and fungi ensure that elements are recycled.

Green plants photosynthesise and make their own food. Animals feed on plants and the energy passes along food chains.

Bacteria and fungi cause decay. They are decomposers. Food that is not preserved will quickly decay.

This turtle mite is a detritivore. Detritivores feed on dead and decaying organisms.

Elements such as carbon and nitrogen are recycled by decomposers.

CONTENTS

How does a plant lose water?

Transpiration is water loss from a plant leaf. The water **evaporates** from the surface of the leaf.

Transpiration is affected by:

- temperature
- amount of light
- wind
- **humidity** (the amount of water in the air).

Experiment to show the effect of light on transpiration rate

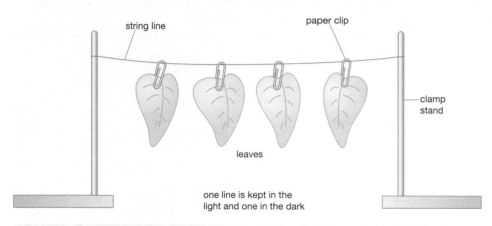

FIGURE 4: Experiment to show the effect of light on transpiration rate. Why are some leaves kept in the light and some in the dark?

Leaves from the same type of plant that are about the same size are weighed. They are then attached to string lines. One of the lines is kept in the light and the other line is kept in the dark for 1 day. The leaves are then re-weighed.

The average loss in weight of leaves kept in the dark is compared to the average loss in weight of leaves kept in the light. Loss of water in transpiration causes leaves to lose weight.

DID YOU KNOW?

On a sunny day an average tree will lose about 150 litres of water – enough to take a bath!

DID YOU KNOW?

The largest known tree roots belonged to a fig tree. Its roots were 120 m long.

QUESTIONS

11 Choose one of the following words to describe the process of clothes drying.

evaporation   **transpiration**   **photosynthesis**

12 What type of weather is good for drying clothes?

13 **a** What is water loss from a plant leaf called?

b Suggest how:

i) windy **ii)** warm **iii)** humid

conditions could be set up in the laboratory to investigate their effects on transpiration rate.

...*evaporate* ...*humidity*

How to reduce water loss

When plants are first put into a garden their roots do not take up a lot of water. Gardeners protect them so that they do not lose too much water from their leaves. This prevents wilting.

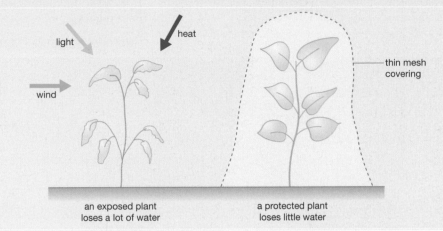

FIGURE 5: Comparing water loss by transpiration from a normal plant and a protected plant.

A high rate of transpiration happens when:

- light intensity increases
- temperature increases
- air movement (wind) increases
- humidity (amount of water in the atmosphere) falls.

FIGURE 6: Cacti plants live in dry hot deserts. Can you suggest why they have very small leaves?

QUESTIONS

14 What weather conditions cause a low rate of transpiration?

15 Explain why cacti must maintain a low rate of transpiration.

16 When plants are protected from wind they grow better. Suggest why.

How is transpiration rate affected?

- When light intensity increases, the stomata open. This allows more water to escape.
- As the temperature increases, the random movement of water molecules increases and more water escapes.
- Wind causes more water molecules near stomata to be removed. This increases evaporation and diffusion of water from inside the leaf.
- In dry conditions there is a very low concentration of water molecules outside the leaf. This causes more diffusion of water from inside the leaf to the outside.

Marram grass

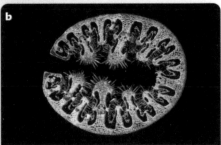

FIGURE 7: **a** Marram grass grows on exposed sand dunes. **b** To reduce transpiration it has leaves with buried stomata surrounded by leaf hairs. The leaves are curled so the stomata are surrounded by high humidity and are not exposed to wind.

QUESTIONS

17 Explain why you should not transplant young plants on a hot windy day.

18 How is Marram grass adapted to live on sand dunes?

19 The stomata of Marram grass may remain open when the plant is short of water and wilting. Suggest why.

Plants need minerals too

You will find out:

- why plants need fertilisers
- which minerals are in fertilisers
- what the minerals are used for

Slash and burn

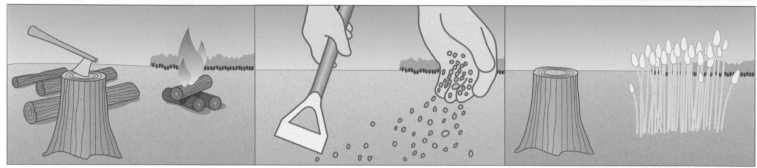

trees cut down and burned

wheat seeds planted in the warm ash and covered with soil

crops harvested after six weeks

Thousands of years ago people struggled to grow crops for food. They cut down trees and burned them. This was called 'slash and burn'. They planted their crops. After a few years their crops were poor so they had to move on. The plants had used up the chemicals in the soil.

Fertilisers

Modern farmers put **fertilisers** on their crop plants. They can then grow the same crop in the same field for several years.

A fertiliser contains **minerals** such as:

- nitrates, containing **nitrogen** (chemical symbol, N)
- phosphates, containing **phosphorus** (P)
- **potassium** (K)
- **magnesium** (Mg).

Plants use these minerals to grow.

Fertilisers can be natural, such as manure, or manufactured.

In a manufactured fertiliser the amount of each mineral can be controlled. This is done because different plants need different minerals at different stages of growth.

FIGURE 1: Spreading slurry (liquid manure) on a field. Why do farmers fertilise their fields?

DID YOU KNOW?

The longest running experiment in the world is at Rothamsted Research. Crops have been grown in the same fields using fertilisers for over 60 years.

QUESTIONS

1. Why did early farmers have poor crops?
2. Which chemical elements have the symbols N, P and K?
3. Why do plants need minerals?
4. Name **two** types of fertiliser.

...fertiliser ...magnesium ...mineral

What minerals do plants need?

NITRATES
- A plant uses nitrates to make proteins.
- Proteins are needed for growth.

PHOSPHATES
- A plant uses phosphates in respiration (releasing energy).
- Phosphates are also needed for growth, especially in roots.

POTASSIUM COMPOUNDS
- Plants use these in respiration and in photosynthesis.

MAGNESIUM COMPOUNDS
- A plant needs these in photosynthesis.

What happens to these minerals?

- Nitrogen in the nitrates is used to make amino acids.
- Amino acids are joined together to make different proteins such as enzymes.

- Phosphorus in phosphates is used to make cell membranes and DNA.
- DNA carries genetic information.

- Potassium is used to help make some enzymes. Enzymes speed up chemical reactions.
- Enzymes are needed in photosynthesis and respiration.

- Magnesium is used to make chlorophyll molecules.

QUESTIONS

5 Which minerals are needed for photosynthesis?
6 Which minerals are needed for respiration?
7 Which minerals are needed for growth?
8 Suggest why a gardener gives his plants fertiliser every week in the summer months.

QUESTIONS

9 Which elements are used to make enzymes?
10 Why are enzymes important to a plant?
11 Which element helps to make a plant green?
12 Which element helps to make DNA?

...nitrogen ...phosphorus ...potassium

Roses are red, violets are blue...

SELF-CHECK ACTIVITY

STEP 1

The solution from the beakers or vase moves up the flower stem. What are the vessels called that the solution travels through?

CONTEXT

Many people know that *Alice in Wonderland* was written by Lewis Carroll. In fact his real name was Charles Dodgson and he was a Professor of Mathematics. Many of the ideas in his two books relate to problems of logic, but Dodgson would also have been aware of scientific experiments that were popular at the time. Changing the colour of flowers was one of these. It is very likely that he made the playing-card figures in *Alice in Wonderland*, shown in this scene, paint the roses a different colour (particularly since they started out white) as a reference to this.

You can do the experiment at home. You need some white flowers, such as carnations, and some food colouring. Add several drops of food colouring to a vase full of water. Place the flowers in the vase and then leave them for a few hours. The colour will appear in the flower petals.

Now remove the flowers and make a transverse (horizontal) cut through the stems (be very careful using a knife) and you will see tiny coloured dots on the cut face of the stem.

If you choose a kind of plant with multiple white flowers on one stem it is even possible to get different flowers on the same stem to be different colours! Slit the stem vertically part of the way up from its base so that the end is in two or three parts, and place each part in a small beaker. Support the stem. Put a different coloured food colouring in each beaker and leave for a few hours.

STEP 3

What makes the solution travel up the stem against gravity?

STEP 4

Water travels up the stem into the flowers. Why do the flowers not become bloated with water?

Cutting through the stem of a flower that has been in food colouring for several hours shows a number of dark dots. What are these?

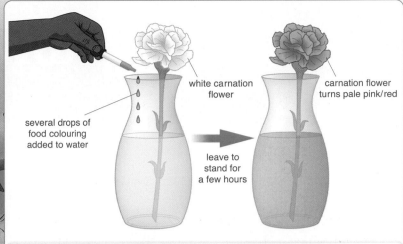

several drops of food colouring added to water

white carnation flower

leave to stand for a few hours

carnation flower turns pale pink/red

Turning a white flower a different colour using food colouring.

What do you think would happen if the experiment was repeated with black ink instead of food colouring? Remember that black ink is not a pure substance — it is made from a number of different coloured inks.

Maximise your grade

These sentences show what you need to be including in your work. Use these to improve your work and to be successful.

Grade	Answer includes...
F	Know that xylem cells carry water up stems.
	Understand that the ink-coloured dots show which parts of the stem carry water and the food colouring.
	Understand that the ink-coloured dots show the cut ends of groups of xylem cells.
	Know that in young stems and leaves the groups of xylem cells are called vascular bundles.
C	Explain that the solution is pushed up the stem by root pressure (water being absorbed by roots), transpiration pull (evaporation of water from the leaves) and capillarity (because xylem tubes are extremely narrow).
	Explain that the water is used in photosynthesis or lost in transpiration from leaves.
A	Combine the ideas that black ink contains different chemicals and plant roots are able to selectively absorb minerals to explain why different colours appear in the petals.
	Explain how the carrier system in the membrane of root hair cells uses energy and absorbs different colours, therefore different colours will appear.

Energy flow

You will find out:

- about energy transfers in food chains
- about pyramids of number and pyramids of biomass
- about efficiency of energy transfers

Food chains

There are about 10 million different animals and plants in the world. All the time new ones are being discovered and some become extinct.

All animals and plants depend on each other.

 Remember, when drawing food chains the direction of the arrow is important. It shows the flow of energy.

Food chains

Each time an organism is eaten, **energy** is transferred from that organism. This energy transfer is shown in a **food chain**.

The energy at the start of a food chain comes from the Sun. Plants use this energy in photosynthesis. Plants are called **producers** because they produce food.

All other organisms in a food chain are called **consumers** because they get their food from other organisms.

Food chains can be linked to form **food webs**.

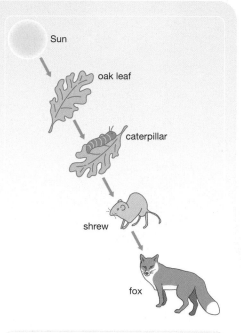

FIGURE 1: A food chain. Which organisms are the consumers?

QUESTIONS

1. Name **four** animals and **two** plants in the woodland scene above.
2. Where does the energy in a food chain come from?
3. Why are plants called producers?

...carnivore ...consumer ...energy ...food chain ...food web ...herbivore

Food pyramids

The links in food chains and food webs show different **trophic** levels.

Energy is passed from one organism to another and each organism is at a different trophic level.

The numbers of organisms at different trophic levels can be counted and the information can be shown in a **pyramid of numbers**. An animal that eats plants is called a **herbivore**. An animal that eats other animals is called a **carnivore**.

A **pyramid of biomass** is a better way of showing trophic levels. The mass of the organisms is used. However, there are changes in mass over time.

As energy flows along a food chain, some is used up in growth. At each trophic level as much as 90 per cent of the energy is transferred into other less useful forms such as heat.

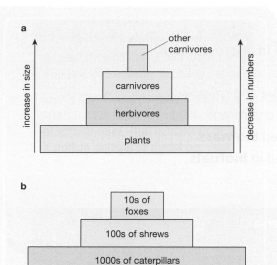

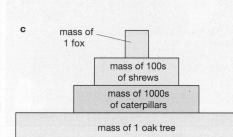

FIGURE 2: a A pyramid of numbers; **b** a woodland food chain does not show a pyramid shape because only one large tree supports all the other organisms; **c** a pyramid of biomass of the same food chain.

Efficiency of energy transfer

The shape of a pyramid of biomass shows that the energy level decreases with increasing trophic level.

Because each trophic level 'loses' up to 90 per cent of the available energy, the length of a food chain is limited to a small number of links. An animal at the end of a long food chain is vulnerable since it depends on earlier food links not being interrupted.

The efficiency of energy transfer can be calculated.

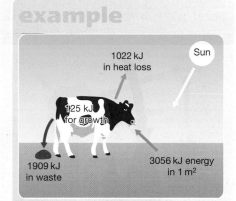

There are 3056 kJ of energy in grass and only 125 kJ are used for a cow's growth. The efficiency of energy transfer can be calculated:

$$\text{efficiency} = \frac{\text{energy used for growth (output)}}{\text{energy supplied (input)}}$$

efficiency = 0.04 or 4%

This shows that the energy transfer to humans from beef is very inefficient.

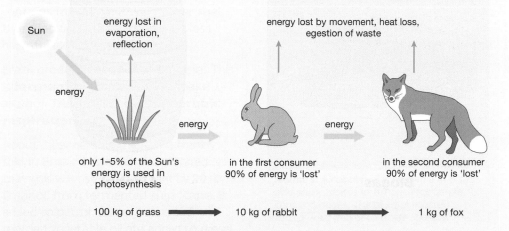

FIGURE 3: Energy flow in a food chain. In what ways is energy lost in a food chain?

QUESTIONS

4   What type of organisms are at the start of a food chain?

5   Is a fox mainly a herbivore or a carnivore?

6   Why does a fox depend on grass?

QUESTIONS

7   Explain why food chains rarely have more than five links.

8   Explain why humans would have a better energy efficiency if they were vegetarians.

Caesium reacts with water in a spectacular way!

Elements are the building blocks of life. They join up in a huge variety of ways to make us and all that is around us. The 92 elements are arranged in groups in the periodic table.

Sodium is also in group 1. It is an element. It has one electron to lose to make it stable. It reacts with oxygen, water and chlorine vigorously to make stable compounds.

Caesium is in group 1 of the periodic table. There are eight groups in total. Elements in group 1 are called the alkali metals. Elements in group 7 are called the halogens. Elements in group 8 are called the Noble gases.

Water is a compound. It is made up of the elements hydrogen and oxygen. Water can be split up into its elements by electrolysis

What are atoms like?

You will find out:

- about the structure of atoms
- about the relative charges and relative masses of electrons, protons and neutrons
- why atoms are neutral

Atoms are the building blocks of all matter, both living and non-living. They can join together in millions of different ways to make all the materials around us. They even join together to make us!

We are made of complex materials. We can explain how simple materials are made using ideas and models of atoms. These ideas have changed over the years but now scientists believe atoms are made of three important particles – protons, electrons and neutrons.

Coloured image of gold atoms on a layer of graphite atoms.

Atoms

An atom is made up of a **nucleus** that is surrounded by **electrons**.

- The nucleus carries a positive charge.
- Electrons that surround the nucleus each carry a negative charge.

Each atom has an **atomic number**. This number is written next to the **symbol** of an **element** in the **periodic table** (see page 258).

If the atomic number of an element is known, it can be identified by looking on the periodic table.

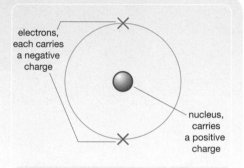

electrons, each carries a negative charge

nucleus, carries a positive charge

FIGURE 1: The structure of an atom.

Watch Out In an atom there are the same number of positive charges in its nucleus as there are negatively charged electrons around it, so an atom is neutral.

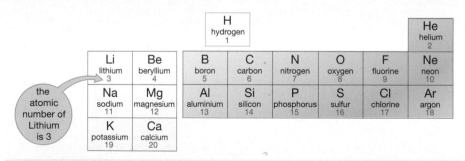

the atomic number of Lithium is 3

						H hydrogen 1		He helium 2
Li lithium 3	Be beryllium 4	B boron 5	C carbon 6	N nitrogen 7	O oxygen 8	F fluorine 9	Ne neon 10
Na sodium 11	Mg magnesium 12	Al aluminium 13	Si silicon 14	P phosphorus 15	S sulfur 16	Cl chlorine 17	Ar argon 18
K potassium 19	Ca calcium 20						

FIGURE 2: Part of the periodic table. What is the name of the element that has an atomic number of 12?

▫▫ QUESTIONS ▫▫

1. What is the charge on a nucleus?
2. What is the charge on an electron?
3. What is the charge on an atom?
4. Use part of the periodic table above to identify the name of the element with an atomic number of 16.

...atomic number ...electron ...element ...isotope ...mass number

More on atoms

The nucleus of an atom is made up of **protons** and **neutrons**.

> The atomic number is the number of protons in an atom.

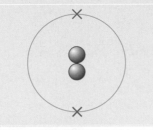

FIGURE 3: A helium atom. (Neutrons not shown.)

The atomic number for helium is 2 because it has two protons.

Neutrons have no charge. There are two neutrons in a helium nucleus.

Mass number

- The relative mass of a proton is 1.
- The relative mass of a neutron is also 1.

> The **mass number** is the total number of protons and neutrons in an atom.

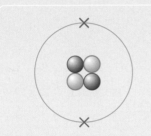

FIGURE 4: Helium has two protons and two neutrons. Helium has a mass number of 4.

Isotopes

There are some elements that have the same atomic number but different mass numbers. These are called **isotopes**.

 It is because a helium atom, He, has two protons that it has an atomic number of 2 – not the other way around.

QUESTIONS

Use the table to help you to answer the questions.

	Charge	Mass
electron	−1	0.0005 (zero)
proton	+1	1
neutron	0	1

5 What is the mass of **one** proton?

6 What is the mass of **one** electron?

7 What is the charge on a proton?

8 What is an isotope?

Why are atoms neutral?

An atom is **neutral** because it has an equal number of electrons and protons. The positive charges balance out the negative charges.

If a particle has an atomic number of 11, a mass number of 23 and a neutral charge, it must be a sodium atom.

Atomic number	11
Mass number	23
Charge	0
	sodium atom

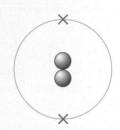

If an element has the symbol $^{14}_{6}C$ it has no charge so it is an atom. It has six protons and a mass of 14. It must therefore have eight (14 − 6) neutrons. $^{14}_{6}C$ is sometimes written as carbon-14.

FIGURE 5: A proton has a positive charge. An electron has a negative charge. This atom is neutral because it has the same number of protons and electrons. (Neutrons not shown.)

> Isotopes of an element have different numbers of neutrons in their atoms.

Isotope	Electrons	Protons	Neutrons
$^{1}_{1}H$	1	1	0
$^{2}_{1}H$	1	1	1
$^{3}_{1}H$	1	1	2

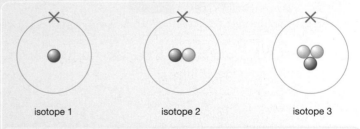

isotope 1   isotope 2   isotope 3

FIGURE 6: Isotopes. What is different in isotopes of the same element?

QUESTIONS

Use the periodic table on page 258 to help you to answer the questions.

9 What is the atom with atomic number 8 and mass number 16?

10 What is the isotope that has 17 protons and 18 neutrons?

The periodic table

There are just over 100 elements.

These elements are listed in the periodic table (see page 258).

> An element is a substance that cannot be broken down chemically.
> An element contains the same type of atom.

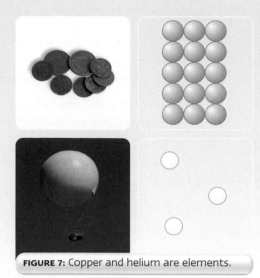

FIGURE 7: Copper and helium are elements.

If two elements join together (chemically combine) a **compound** is made.

> A compound is a substance that contains at least two elements chemically combined.

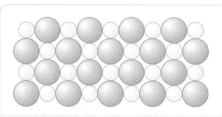

magnesium (element)   **oxygen (element)**

FIGURE 8: Magnesium and oxygen react to produce magnesium oxide, a compound.

The elements in a compound can be seen from the formula, by using the periodic table (see page 258).

example

The compound magnesium oxide, MgO, contains Mg, magnesium and O, oxygen.

QUESTIONS

11   Write down if the following substances are elements or compounds.
     copper   copper chloride   copper sulfate

12   Write down the names of the elements in potassium chloride.

13   Write down the names of the elements in NaF.

14   Write down the names of the elements in $MgSO_4$.

...*compound   ...electron pattern*

You will find out:

- that there are just over 100 elements
- about the make-up of elements
- about the make-up of compounds
- how to identify the elements in a compound

The arrangement of electrons in atoms

The elements in the periodic table are arranged in ascending atomic number.

> ## example
>
> The atomic number of hydrogen is 1, of carbon is 6 and of sodium is 11 (see page 258 for the periodic table).

The same number of electrons occupies the space around the protons of the nucleus.

> ## example
>
> Oxygen has an atomic number of 8. It has eight electrons in the space around the nucleus.

Electrons occupy **shells**. The electron shell nearest to the nucleus takes up to two electrons. The second shell takes up to eight electrons.

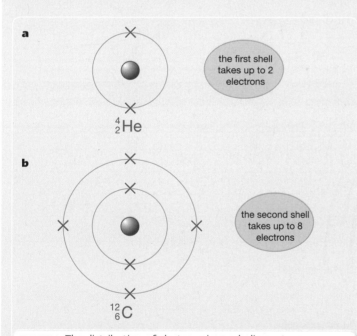

a

the first shell takes up to 2 electrons

$^4_2$He

b

the second shell takes up to 8 electrons

$^{12}_6$C

FIGURE 9: The distribution of electrons in **a** a helium atom; **b** a carbon atom. What is the maximum number of electrons in the second shell of an atom?

> ### QUESTIONS
>
> 15 What is the atomic number of the element sodium?
>
> 16 How many electrons does an atom of sodium have?
>
> 17 Draw a diagram to show the pattern of electrons in a sodium atom.

Electronic structure

Each element has an **electron pattern** (**electronic structure**).

The electronic structure of each of the first 20 elements can be worked out using:

- the atomic number of the element
- the maximum number of electrons in each shell.

The third shell takes up to eight electrons before the fourth shell starts to fill. The fourth shell can take up to 18 electrons.

> ## example
>
> The atomic number of lithium, Li, is 3. So the first two electrons of the lithium atom fill the first shell. The third electron goes into the second shell. The electronic structure is 2,1.

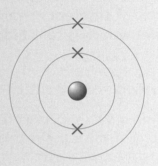

- Neon, Ne, has an atomic number of 10 so its electronic structure is 2, 8.
- Aluminium, Al, has an atomic number of 13 so electrons start to occupy the third shell and its electronic structure is 2, 8, 3.
- Calcium, Ca, has an atomic number of 20 so electrons start to occupy the fourth shell and its electronic structure is 2, 8, 8, 2.

> ### QUESTIONS
>
> Use the periodic table on page 258 to help you to answer the questions.
>
> 18 What is the electronic structure of F that has atomic number 9?
>
> 19 What is the electronic structure of Mg that has atomic number 12?
>
> 20 What is the electronic structure of K?
>
> 21 What is the element with electronic structure 2, 8, 3?

How atoms combine – Ionic bonding

You will find out:
- that an ion is a charged atom or group of atoms
- how to recognise an ion, an atom and a molecule from given formulae

Bonds

Atoms join together, or bond, in many different ways. They may join by transferring electrons. They may bond by sharing electrons. These different types of bond allow atoms to join in a huge number of ways to make millions of different compounds. One way atoms bond is by electron transfer, which is called ionic bonding.

Forming ions and molecules

An **atom** is the smallest particle that can bond with another particle. An atom can be recognised from its symbol. It either has one capital letter or one capital letter and one lower case letter (see the periodic table on page 258).

The symbol for an atom has no numbers and no charge. The symbol for a magnesium atom is shown below.

Mg   **magnesium**

An **ion** is a charged atom or group of atoms. It has a positive or negative charge on it. A calcium ion has two positive charges as shown below.

Ca^{2+}   **calcium ion**

A **molecule** has more than one atom in its formula and no charge.

CO_2   **carbon dioxide**

The table shows some examples of elements as atoms, ions and molecules.

Atom	Ion	Molecule
H	H^+	H_2
O	O^{2-}	H_2O
Mg	Mg^{2+}	MgO
Cl	Cl^-	$MgCl_2$
Na	Na^+	NaOH
S	SO_4^{2-}	$MgSO_4$

QUESTIONS

Use the table above to help you to answer these questions.
1   Write down the:
   a symbol for an atom
   b formula for an ion
   c formula for a molecule.
2   What is the symbol for an atom of oxygen?
3   What is the formula for a magnesium ion?
4   What is the formula for a hydrogen molecule?
5   How many atoms are there in one molecule of magnesium oxide?

...atom ...'dot and cross' model ...electrostatic ...ion ...lattice ...metal

Why do atoms form bonds?

An atom usually has too many electrons or too few electrons to be stable.

- An atom that has too many electrons needs to lose them. These are **metal** atoms.
- An atom that has too few electrons needs to gain them. These are **non-metal** atoms.

Ionic bonds

If an atom loses electrons a **positive ion** is formed.

- If an atom loses one electron a (positive) $^+$ion is formed, for example $Na \longrightarrow Na^+$.
- If an atom loses two electrons a (positive) 2^+ ion is formed, for example $Mg \longrightarrow Mg^{2+}$.

If an atom gains electrons a **negative ion** is formed.

- If an atom gains one electron a (negative) $^-$ion is formed, for example $F \longrightarrow F^-$.
- If an atom gains two electrons a (negative) 2^- ion is formed, for example $O \longrightarrow O^{2-}$.

A metal atom has extra electrons in its outer shell. It needs to lose these electrons to be stable. The electrons transfer from the metal atom to a non-metal atom to form a stable pair.

A non-metal atom has 'spaces' in its outer shell. It needs to gain electrons to be stable. The electrons transfer to the non-metal atom from the metal atom to make a stable pair.

- The metal atom becomes a positive ion.
- The non-metal atom becomes a negative ion.
- The positive ion and the negative ion then attract one another.
- They attract to a number of other ions to make a solid **lattice**.

When sodium chloride is in solution it conducts electricity.

Molten (melted) magnesium oxide and sodium chloride conduct electricity.

QUESTIONS

6　What is the difference between a metal atom and a non-metal atom?
　　Use ideas about electrons in your answer.

7　Explain how a positive ion is made from a neutral atom.

8　Explain how metals and non-metals combine.

9　When does sodium chloride conduct electricity?

Describing ionic bonding

We use the **'dot and cross' model** to describe ionic bonding.

example

Sodium chloride is a solid lattice made up of many pairs of ions held together by **electrostatic** attraction.

- Sodium forms a positive sodium ion.
- Chlorine forms a negative chloride ion.

The outer electron of sodium is transferred to the outer shell of the chlorine atom.

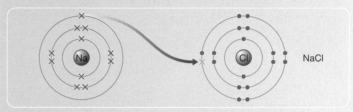

The sodium ion and the chloride ion are held together by attraction of opposite charges.

example

The bonding in magnesium oxide works in exactly the same way, except that the magnesium atom loses two electrons and the oxygen gains the two electrons to become an oxide ion.

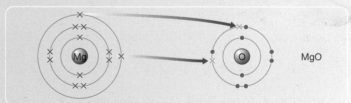

The 'dot and cross' model looks like this:

Other examples can be found on page 101.

QUESTIONS

10　Explain why the formula for aluminium chloride is $AlCl_3$.
　　Use ideas about transferring electrons.

Properties of sodium chloride and magnesium oxide

Sodium chloride

- Sodium chloride has a high **melting point**.
- It **dissolves** in water. Sometimes this water **evaporates**.
- It does not conduct electricity when it is a solid.

You will find out:
- about the properties of sodium chloride and magnesium oxide
- about the giant ionic lattice structure of sodium chloride and magnesium oxide

FIGURE 2: Sodium chloride can form giant crystals.

FIGURE 3: A saltpan in Crete. The water evaporates and salt is left.

Magnesium oxide

- Magnesium oxide has a very high melting point.
- It does not conduct electricity when it is a solid.

▮▮ QUESTIONS ▮▮

11 Describe the melting point of sodium chloride.

12 Is sodium chloride soluble or insoluble in water?

13 When does sodium chloride not conduct electricity?

14 Describe the melting point of magnesium oxide.

...dissolve ...evaporate ...giant ionic lattice

More on ionic bonding

'Dot and cross' models for sodium chloride and magnesium oxide are given on page 99. Other compounds that bond using ionic bonds are sodium oxide and magnesium chloride.

Sodium only has one electron to lose, but oxygen needs to gain two electrons. Two sodium atoms are needed to bond with one oxygen atom.

On the other hand, magnesium needs to lose two electrons, but chlorine can only gain one electron. So one magnesium atom needs two chlorine atoms to achieve an ionic bond and make magnesium chloride.

Each atom has either gained or lost the correct number of electrons to achieve a complete outer shell. The outer shell needs eight electrons. It is called a **stable octet**.

If aluminium makes an Al^{3+} ion and chlorine makes a Cl^- ion we can work out that the formula of aluminium chloride is $AlCl_3$.

The structure of sodium chloride or magnesium oxide is a **giant ionic lattice**, where positive ions are electrostatically attracted to negative ions.

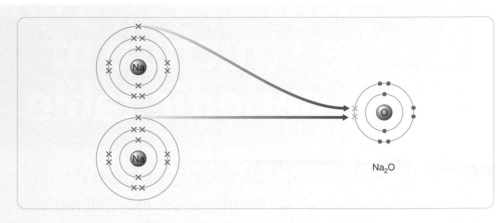

Na_2O

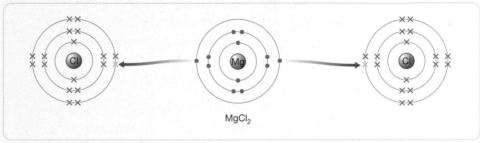

$MgCl_2$

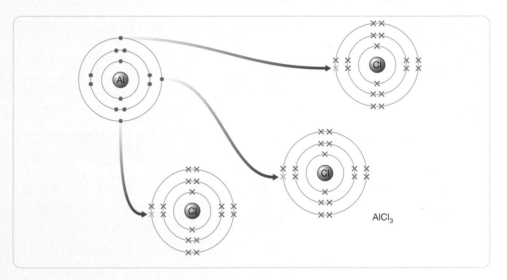

$AlCl_3$

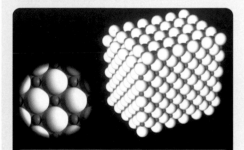

FIGURE 4: There is a strong attraction between positive and negative ions of sodium chloride, forming a giant lattice.

Physical properties

Some of the physical properties of sodium chloride and magnesium oxide are:

- strong attraction between positive and negative ions so they have high melting points
- ions cannot move in the solid so it does not conduct electricity
- ions can move in solution or in a molten liquid so these conduct electricity.

QUESTIONS

15 What is a stable octet?

16 Draw a diagram to show how an electron is transferred from a lithium atom to a fluorine atom.

17 Draw a 'dot and cross diagram' to show lithium fluoride.

18 Draw a 'dot and cross diagram' to show calcium chloride.

19 Describe the structure of sodium chloride.

20 Why does magnesium oxide have a high melting point?

21 Why do ionic solids not conduct electricity?

22 Why do molten liquids of ionic compounds conduct electricity?

...melting point   ...stable octet

Covalent bonding and the structure of the periodic table

How do atoms join together?

Atoms can join together by transferring electrons. However, others may bond by sharing electrons. By sharing electrons between atoms, the compounds have different properties and do not conduct electricity. This type of bonding is known as covalent bonding.

Molecules

A **molecule** forms when two or more non-metal **atoms** bond together.

If a molecule has the formula O_2, we can see that it has two oxygen atoms in its **molecular formula**, so the total number of atoms is two.

Its **displayed formula** looks like this: It looks like this as a model:

FIGURE 1: A molecule forms when two or more atoms bond together.

If a molecule has the formula CO_2, we can see that it has one carbon atom and two oxygen atoms in its molecular formula, so the total number of atoms is three.

Its displayed formula looks like this: It looks like this as a model:

QUESTIONS

1   How many atoms are there in a molecule of sulfur, S_6?

2   How many different types of atom are there in a molecule of H_2SO_4?

3   How many atoms are there in total in a molecule of H_2SO_4?

4   How many atoms are there in the methane molecule shown on the right?

...atom ...covalent ...displayed formula ...'dot and cross' model

Covalent bonding

Non-metals combine together by sharing **electrons**.

This is called **covalent** bonding.

example

A molecule of water is made up of three atoms. There are two hydrogen atoms and one oxygen atom in water.

■ Oxygen has six electrons in its outer shell. So it needs two more electrons to be complete.

■ Hydrogen atoms each have one electron in their only shell. So the oxygen outer shell is shared with each of the hydrogen electrons.

■ In this way each of the hydrogen atoms has a share of two more electrons so the shell is full.

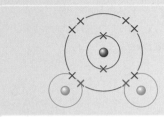

FIGURE 2: A molecule of water. The oxygen atom (red) has a share of eight electrons so has a full outer shell. How many electrons does each hydrogen atom share?

example

A molecule of carbon dioxide is also made up of three atoms. There are two oxygen atoms and one carbon atom.

■ Carbon has four electrons in its outer shell. So it needs four more electrons to be complete.

■ Oxygen atoms each have six electrons in their outer shell. So they each need two more electrons to be complete.

■ So each oxygen outer shell is shared with two of the electrons of the carbon outer shell.

■ In this way each of the oxygen atoms has a share of two more electrons so the shell is full.

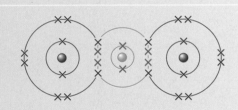

FIGURE 3: A molecule of carbon dioxide. The carbon atom (blue) has a share of eight electrons so has a full outer shell. How many electrons does each oxygen atom share?

Carbon dioxide and water do not conduct electricity because they are covalently bonded.

QUESTIONS

5   Oxygen atoms join as a pair by which type of bonding?

6   Draw a model of hydrogen atoms bonding as H_2.

7   Draw the displayed formula for carbon dioxide.

8   Is carbon dioxide a conductor of electricity or an insulator?

'Dot and cross' models

The formation of simple molecules containing single and double covalent bonds can be represented by **'dot and cross' models**.

example

The following are the 'dot and cross' models for some simple molecules.

H ×• H
H_2

×× Cl ×• Cl ••
Cl_2

•• O ×• C ×• O ••
CO_2

H ×• O ×• H
H_2O

QUESTIONS

9   Draw a 'dot and cross' model of the bonding in methane, CH_4.

10 Draw a 'dot and cross' model of the bonding in NH_3.

Groups and periods in the periodic table

There are two types of bonding.

■ Ionic bonding. Large crystals are bonded by ionic bonds.

■ Covalent bonding. Molecules are bonded by covalent bonds. Examples are carbon dioxide, which is a gas, and water, which is a liquid. These molecules have low melting points.

Elements that are in the same **group** (family) in the periodic table (see page 258 for the whole periodic table) are written in the same vertical **column** on the table.

A group of elements is all the elements in a vertical column of the periodic table. These elements have similar **chemical properties**.

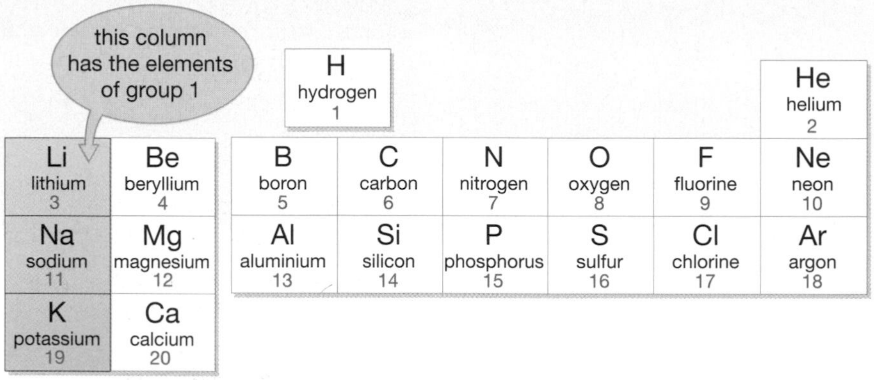

FIGURE 4: Group 1 elements in the periodic table. Can you name the elements in group 1?

Lithium, sodium and potassium are all in group 1.

A **period** of elements is all the elements in a horizontal **row** of the periodic table.

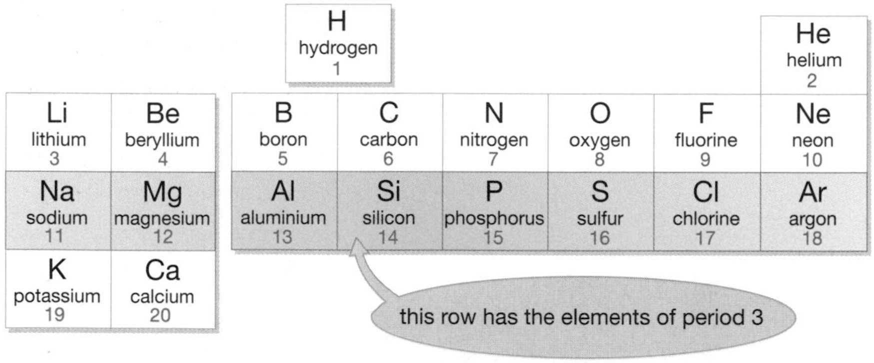

FIGURE 5: Elements from period 3 of the periodic table. Can you list the elements that belong to this period?

You will find out:

- about ionic bonding and covalent bonding
- what a group of elements is and that the group number is the same as the number of electrons in the outer shell
- what a period of elements is and how a period relates to electronic structure
- how the properties of carbon dioxide and water are related to their structure

DID YOU KNOW?

When lithium, sodium and potassium are added to water they all float, fizz and pop and make a gas called hydrogen.

■ QUESTIONS ■

Use the periodic table on page 258 to help you answer these questions.

11 What is a group of elements?

12 Which elements are in group 2?

13 What is a period of elements?

14 Which elements are in period 2?

...chemical property   ...column   ...element   ...group

Group numbers

The **group number** is the same as the number of electrons in the outer shell.

Group 1 elements have one electron in the outer shell.

- Lithium has this electron pattern:

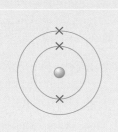

- Sodium has this electron pattern:

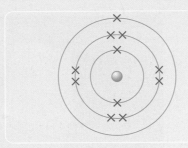

Group 7 elements have seven electrons in the outer shell.

- Fluorine has this electron pattern:

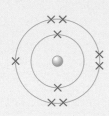

- Chlorine has this electron pattern:

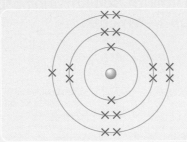

Group 8 elements have eight electrons in the outer shell.

- Neon has this electron pattern:

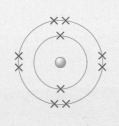

- Argon has this electron pattern:

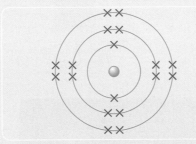

How to tell which period an element belongs to

- If an element has electrons in only one shell it will be found in the first period.
- If an element has electrons in two shells it will be found in the second period.
- If an element has electrons in three shells it will be found in the third period.

Element	Electron pattern	Period
H	1	1
Li	2, 1	2
Na	2, 8, 1	3

QUESTIONS

15 To which group does carbon belong, with electron pattern 2, 4?

16 Explain why oxygen belongs to group 6.

17 To which period does magnesium belong, with electron pattern 2, 8, 2?

18 Explain why nitrogen belongs to period 2.

Predicting chemical properties

Carbon dioxide and water are simple molecules with weak **intermolecular forces** between molecules.

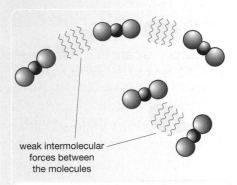

weak intermolecular forces between the molecules

FIGURE 6: Molecules have weak intermolecular forces between them. How does this affect their chemical properties?

The chemical properties of carbon dioxide and water are related to their structure.

- As they have weak intermolecular forces between the molecules they are easy to separate so the substances have low melting points.
- As there are no free electrons available they do not conduct electricity.

QUESTIONS

19 Explain why carbon dioxide has a low melting point.

20 Explain why water does not conduct electricity.

21 The electronic structure of phosphorus looks like this.

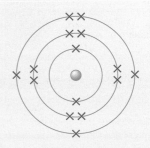

Explain how the structure of phosphorus shows that it is in group 5 and period 3 of the periodic table.

The group 1 elements

You will find out:

- that group 1 metals are known as the alkali metals
- that lithium, sodium and potassium are group 1 metals
- why alkali metals are stored under oil
- how to predict the properties of other alkali metals

The alkali metals

Ever wondered how fireworks are made to have such stunning colours? It is because they have compounds added to them. Sodium compounds, for instance, produce a bright yellow colour against the night sky. Sodium is an element in the periodic table in the first column. When Dmitri Mendeleev first put the elements into an order in his first table, he grouped lithium, sodium and potassium together. We now know these as the group 1 elements.

This is lithium.

Alkali metals

Group 1 metals are called the **alkali metals**.

Alkali metals are stored under oil because they react with air and water.

Alkali metals react vigorously with water.

The order of **reactivity** of the alkali metals with water is:

- sodium is more reactive than lithium
- potassium is more reactive than sodium.

lithium, sodium and potassium are metals in group 1

FIGURE 1: Group 1 metals in the periodic table. What is another name for them?

is more reactive than

is more reactive than

potassium   sodium   lithium

FIGURE 2: The order of reactivity of the alkali metals. Which metal is the most reactive?

QUESTIONS

1 Write down the names of **three** group 1 metals.
2 What do group 1 metals look like when freshly cut?
3 Why are group 1 metals kept under oil?
4 Which metal in group 1 is the least reactive?

...alkali   ...alkali metal   ...density

This picture shows you what can happen if you get pure sodium hydroxide on your skin. It is used in home oven cleaners. The instructions on the bottle tell you to use gloves!

Sodium hydroxide is more dangerous to get into the eyes than acids are. The ions travel to the back of the eyes and can irreversibly damage the retina.

That is why your teacher always tells you to wear safety glasses when handling chemicals, especially alkalis!

Properties of alkali metals

When lithium, sodium and potassium react with water they float on the surface. This is because their **density** is less than the density of water.

A gas is given off. This gas is hydrogen.

The metal reacts with water to form an **alkali**. This is the **hydroxide** of the metal.

- Sodium forms sodium hydroxide.
- Potassium forms potassium hydroxide.

Is there a pattern in the reactivity of alkali metals with water?

- Lithium reacts quickly and vigorously with water.
- Sodium reacts very quickly and very vigorously with water.
- Potassium reacts extremely vigorously with water and produces a lilac flame.

Reactivity of the alkali metals with water increases down group 1.

reactivity increases down the group

The word equations for these reactions are:

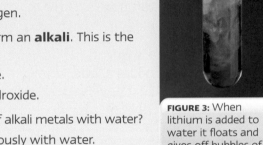

FIGURE 3: When lithium is added to water it floats and gives off bubbles of a colourless gas. What is the gas?

	Melting point in °C	Boiling point in °C
$_3$Li	179	1317
$_{11}$Na	98	892
$_{19}$K	64	774

lithium + water	→	lithium hydroxide + hydrogen
sodium + water	→	sodium hydroxide + hydrogen
potassium + water	→	potassium hydroxide + hydrogen

QUESTIONS

5 Why does sodium float on water?

6 **a** Which gas is given off when sodium reacts with water?

   b How could you test for this gas?

7 Why are the group 1 metals called alkali metals?

8 How does the reactivity of the alkali metals with water change going down the group?

Predicting how other alkali metals react

The word equation for the reaction of sodium and water is:

sodium + water → sodium hydroxide + hydrogen

This can be represented in symbols:

$$Na + H_2O \longrightarrow NaOH + H_2$$

but the equation is not balanced.

The balanced symbol equation for the reaction of sodium metal with water is:

$$2Na + 2H_2O \longrightarrow 2NaOH + H_2$$

The reactivity with water increases down group 1.

$_3$Li
$_{11}$Na
$_{19}$K
$_{37}$Rb
$_{55}$Cs
$_{87}$Fr

You should be able to predict the way that other alkali metals behave from the patterns so far.

For example, how does rubidium react with water?

Does it react more vigorously or less vigorously than potassium?

And, what is the melting point, boiling point, appearance and electrical conductivity of rubidium and caesium?

Think about the trends you have seen so far.

QUESTIONS

9 Write a balanced symbol equation for the reaction of potassium with water.

10 Will the reaction of caesium with water be more vigorous or less vigorous than that of sodium with water?

11 Will the melting point of rubidium be higher or lower than that of lithium?

12 What alkali will be made when caesium reacts with water?

Flaming metals!

- If you put compounds of lithium in a flame, the flame turns red.

- If you put compounds of sodium in a flame, the flame turns yellow.

- If you put compounds of potassium in a flame, the flame turns lilac.

You will find out:

- that compounds of group 1 elements produce coloured flames
- how to use flame colour to find out which alkali metal is present
- how to carry out a flame test
- how the properties of group 1 metals are related to their electronic structure

Whizzbang Firework Company wants to make a new set of 'starburst' fireworks for its anniversary range.

It wants to produce a set of lilac 'starbursts'. The technical department suggests adding potassium chloride to the mix. Would this produce a 'lilac' effect against the night sky?

The department is also asked to produce a starburst with a red effect and one with a yellow effect.

Below is the memo that the department produces.

MEMO

technical department

Suggestions for chemicals to be added to 'starbursts' for anniversary range:

Chemicals	Colour
potassium chloride	lilac
lithium chloride	red
sodium chloride	yellow

QUESTIONS

13 What colour does a compound of sodium produce in a flame?

14 What colour does a compound of potassium produce in a flame?

15 Which chemical produces a red flame?

16 Which chemical produces a yellow flame?

...electron ...ion ...ionic equation

Flame tests

Sancha and Alessia want to test the quality of the chemicals that the Whizzbang firework company is going to add to its fireworks.

There is one test that will ensure the colour is correct.

- Put on safety glasses. Moisten a flame test wire with dilute hydrochloric acid.

- Dip the flame test wire into the sample of solid chemical.

- Hold the flame test wire in a blue Bunsen burner flame.

- Record the colour of the flame in a table.

Alkali metal in the compound	Colour of flame
lithium	red
sodium	yellow
potassium	lilac

These group 1 metals have one **electron** in their outer **shell**.

This is why group 1 metals have similar properties.

17 When performing a flame test what is the flame test wire moistened with?

18 What colour Bunsen burner flame is the test wire and sample held in?

19 What alkali metal compound is indicated by a lilac flame?

20 How many electrons do elements in group 1 have in their outer shell?

Explaining reactivity patterns

Alkali metals have similar properties. This is because when they react their atoms need to lose one electron to form full outer shells. This is then a **stable electronic structure**.

When the atom loses one electron it forms an **ion**. The atom becomes charged. It has more positive charges in its nucleus than negative electrons surrounding it. So the charge is positive. It has made a positive ion.

This can be represented by an equation. It shows the formation of an ion from its atom.

$$Na - e^- \longrightarrow Na^+$$

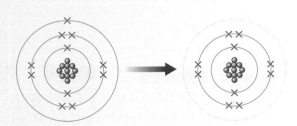

FIGURE 4: How alkali metals achieve a stable electronic structure. 11 protons [+] and 11 electrons [−] make a neutral atom; 11 protons [+] and 10 electrons [−] make a positive ion.

Lithium loses its outer electron from its second shell. Sodium loses its outer electron from its third shell. The third shell is further away from the attractive 'pulling force' of the nucleus. This means that the electron from sodium is more easily lost than the electron from lithium. This is why sodium is more reactive than lithium.

> The easier it is for an atom to lose one electron, the more reactive the alkali metal.

The outer electron of potassium is even further away from the nucleus so is even more easily lost from the atom. So potassium is even more reactive than either sodium or lithium.

Oxidation

If electrons are lost, the process is called **oxidation**.

$$K - e^- \longrightarrow K^+$$

You can see why this process is oxidation from its **ionic equation**. An atom of potassium loses one electron. It now becomes a potassium ion. The potassium ion is a positive ion. This is an example of oxidation.

electron in outer shell is further from the nucleus, there is less attractive force, so the electron is more easily lost

electron in outer shell is closer to the nucleus, there is more attractive force, so the electron is less easily lost

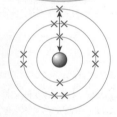

FIGURE 5: The more easily an atom loses its outer electron the more reactive it is.

21 Why does an atom in group 1 lose electrons?

22 Why is sodium more reactive than lithium?

23 What is the process of losing electrons called?

24 Write an equation to show the oxidation reaction for lithium.

Dancing around and delirious with joy!

SELF-CHECK ACTIVITY

STEP 1

From Davy's earlier electrolysis experiments, how do you think he could show that the gas released was hydrogen?

CONTEXT

What do you see when you look at the periodic table? You see a summary of hundreds of pieces of information about elements, brought together in one chart. This information has been discovered by many different scientists from all over the world, but a few people have made a major contribution and one of those was Cornishman Humphry Davy.

Around 1800 there were a number of scientists experimenting with using electricity to break down substances into their component elements. Davy was convinced he could do this to what were then known as the alkali earths. At first he was unsuccessful – he tried passing current through solutions of alkali earths, but this simply released hydrogen. He then tried melting the compounds and passing a current through them. This worked much better and produced tiny beads of pure metal. When beads of one of these metals were dropped on to water they 'skimmed about excitedly with a hissing sound, and soon burned with a lovely lavender light' according to Humphry's brother John.

Davy continued to use electricity to extract elements from compounds in a process we now call electrolysis and he managed to discover magnesium, calcium, barium and strontium. Another of his discoveries was nitrous oxide, or 'laughing gas', which he is said to have breathed large quantities of himself. Then used by dentists as an anaesthetic, Davy used it for fun. It is likely that this and the other gases he sampled affected his health and caused him to die prematurely.

Humphry 'danced around and was delirious with joy' when he saw this lavender light.

STEP 2

What was the metal that, when added to water, 'skimmed about excitedly with a hissing sound, and soon burned with a lovely lavender light'?

STEP 3

Think about the reaction of the metal added to water.

a   If Universal indicator solution was added to the water after the reaction, what colour would it be?

b   What product from the reaction causes this colour change?

c   How does this help to explain the general name given to the group 1 metals?

d   Why is a safety screen necessary during the reaction?

STEP 4

Write down an equation to summarise the reaction.

STEP 5

When Davy wanted to extract pure sodium he started with table salt.

a   Why was this?

b   What is the other element released?

Maximise your grade

These sentences show what you need to be including in your work. Use these to improve your work and to be successful.

Grade	Answer includes...
F	State how to test for hydrogen.
	State the chemical name for table salt and identify the **two** elements in the compound.
	Explain how a flame test can identify the metal and explain why safety precautions are necessary when group 1 metals react with water.
	Write a word equation for the reaction between the metal and water and suggest the colour change for Universal Indicator as it is added to the water after the reaction.
C	State the product of the chemical reaction between the metal and water. Explain, using the terms acid and alkali, why Universal Indicator changes colour in the way it does.
	Use chemical symbols to write an equation for the reaction between the metal and water.
A	Explain why group 1 metals are sometimes known as the 'alkali earth' metals.
	Write a balanced symbol equation for the reaction between the metal and water.

The group 7 elements

Halogens

Group 7 elements are known as the halogens. Halogens have many uses. Chlorine is used to sterilise water and to make pesticides and plastics. Iodine is used to sterilise wounds.

Sodium chloride is used as a preservative, as flavouring and in the manufacture of chlorine.

The halogens

Group 7 elements are called the **halogens**.

Fluorine, chlorine, bromine and iodine are halogens.

Halogens react vigorously with **alkali metals** such as sodium and potassium.

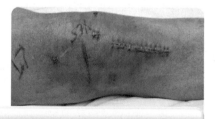

this column has the elements of group 7

FIGURE 1: Group 7 elements in the periodic table. What is another name for them?

The uses of some halogens

a Chlorine is used to sterilise water.

b Chlorine is used to make plastics and pesticides.

c Iodine is used to sterilise wounds.

FIGURE 2: The uses of some halogens.

The uses of sodium chloride

Sodium chloride is used:
a as a preservative

b as a flavouring

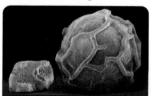

c in the manufacture of chlorine.

FIGURE 3: The uses of sodium chloride.

QUESTIONS

1. What is chlorine used for?
2. Give **one** use of iodine.
3. Which compound of a halogen is used in the manufacture of chlorine?
4. With which type of metal do halogens react vigorously?

...alkali metal   ...halogen   ...ion

Group 7 trends

There is a **trend** in the physical appearance of the halogens at room temperature. Chlorine is a gas, bromine is a liquid and iodine is a solid.

Reactions between alkali metals and halogens

When alkali metals react with halogens there is a vigorous reaction. A **metal halide** is made.

- When lithium reacts with chlorine the metal halide made is lithium chloride.
- When potassium reacts with bromine the metal halide made is potassium bromide.
- When sodium reacts with chlorine the metal halide made is sodium chloride.

FIGURE 4: At room temperature chlorine is a green gas, bromine is an orange liquid and iodine is a grey solid.

FIGURE 5: What is made when green chlorine gas and sodium metal react?

Constructing word equations

lithium	+	chlorine	$\longrightarrow$	lithium chloride
sodium	+	bromine	$\longrightarrow$	sodium bromide
potassium	+	iodine	$\longrightarrow$	potassium iodide

▦▦ QUESTIONS ▦▦

5 Which halogen is an orange liquid at room temperature?

6 What is the appearance of iodine at room temperature?

7 What metal halide is made when potassium reacts with bromine?

8 Write down the word equation for the reaction between sodium and chlorine.

Balancing equations

It is now possible to construct a balanced symbol equation for the reaction of an alkali metal with a halogen.

Step 1

Write down the symbols for the alkali metal (potassium, K) and the halogen (chlorine, Cl_2). These are the **reactants**.

The '2' in Cl_2 means there are two bonded atoms in the molecule of chlorine. This number cannot be changed!

Step 2

Write down the formula for the product (potassium chloride, KCl). Notice that only one chloride **ion** is joined to one potassium ion. This leaves a 'spare' chlorine ion without another ion to join to.

$(K + Cl_2 \longrightarrow KCl)$

Step 3

Join this spare second chlorine ion to a second potassium ion, represented by a large '2' in front of the symbol K, to give 2K. So we have two potassium ions joined to two chloride ions, giving 2KCl.

$2K + Cl_2 \longrightarrow 2KCl$

The product is therefore 2KCl.

▦▦ QUESTIONS ▦▦

9 What is the formula for a molecule of bromine?

10 Why is the formula of chlorine gas written as Cl_2?

11 Why is KCl not written as KCl_2?

12 Write a balanced symbol equation for the formation of lithium chloride from its elements.

Crystals in metals

A metal has a structure that contains **crystals**.

The particles in a solid metal are:

- close together
- in a regular arrangement.

FIGURE 5: A magnified thin section of brass showing its grain structure.

Superconductors

At very low temperatures some metals become **superconductors**.

Superconductors can be used to make super-fast circuits and to **levitate** magnets.

The first *Maglev* train (*magnetic levitation*) made for use in England ran between Birmingham International Railway station and Birmingham Airport.

QUESTIONS

8 What do metals contain as part of their structure?
9 Describe the arrangement of particles in a metal.
10 When can some metals become superconductors?
11 How can superconductors be used to make trains run faster?

...critical temperature ...crystals ...levitate

Conductors

When metals conduct electricity, electrons in the metal move.

Copper, silver and gold conduct electricity very well but surprisingly do not become superconductors.

Superconductors

Superconductors are materials that conduct electricity with little or no **resistance**.

The electrical resistance of mercury suddenly drops to zero at −268.8 °C. This phenomenon is called **superconductivity**. The temperature at which it occurs is called the **critical temperature**.

There are two types of superconductor:

- type I, which are metals
- type II, which are alloys.

The Meissner effect

When a substance goes from its normal state to a superconducting state, it no longer has any magnetic fields inside it. This is called the Meissner effect.

- If a small magnet is brought near the superconductor, it is repelled.
- If a small permanent magnet is placed above the superconductor, it levitates.

FIGURE 6: It looks like magic! This small permanent magnet is levitating above a superconductor.

The potential benefits of superconductors are:

- loss-free power transmission
- super-fast electronic circuits
- powerful electromagnets.

QUESTIONS

12 What happens to mercury at a temperature of −268.8 °C?

13 What is the 'critical temperature'?

14 What is the Meissner effect?

15 Find out from Internet resources and books how far research has succeeded in making **two** potential uses of superconductors a reality.

More on delocalised electrons

A metal conducts electricity because delocalised electrons within its structure can move easily.

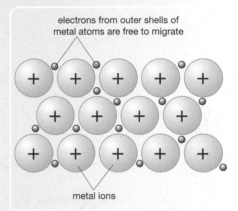

electrons from outer shells of metal atoms are free to migrate

metal ions

FIGURE 7: The structure of a metal. What carries electric charge when a current passes through a metal?

Difficulties of superconductors

There needs to be a good deal of development work before the true potential of superconductors is realised.

- They work only at very low temperatures.
- Superconductors that function at 20 °C need to be developed.

QUESTIONS

16 Compare the reasons why a metal is a good electrical conductor and a non-metal is not.

17 Discuss the usefulness of superconductors.

18 Find out **one** use of superconductors used in healthcare.

Module summary

Concept map

Atoms consist of a positive nucleus surrounded by negative electrons.

Electrons are arranged in a pattern, or configuration. The outer shell of electrons needs to be full to be stable.

Atoms and bonding
Atoms join together to make molecules or large crystal structures. There are two ways in which atoms can bond:

- by making ions, or
- by sharing electrons.

Ions form when atoms lose or gain electrons to make a full outer shell. Ions are either positive or negative.

Atoms can share electrons to make molecules containing two or more atoms. This is called covalent bonding.

Group 1 metals react vigorously with water to make alkaline solutions.

Periodic table
The periodic table lists all elements in order of their atomic number.

The periodic table lists elements in groups. These elements have similar properties. They are in groups according to the pattern of their electrons.

Group 7 elements are called the halogens. They have seven electrons in their outer shell.

Pure water does not conduct electricity. If sulfuric acid is added, water decomposes to give hydrogen and oxygen gases.

Electrolysis
Electrolysis is the decomposition of a substance using electricity.

Aluminium is made from the electrolysis of bauxite. The mineral has to be purified before it is used. The aluminium is deposited at the cathode.

Iron, gold, silver, copper, nickel and chromium are transition metals. They are used in a wide range of objects. Mercury is used in thermometers as it is a liquid metal at room temperature.

Transition metals and metal structure

Transition metal compounds are usually coloured.

The compounds often dissolve in water to make coloured solutions, which react with sodium hydroxide to make coloured precipitates.

Module quiz

1. What are the **three** particles that make up an atom?

2. What is made up of two or more elements chemically combined?

3. What number of electrons can the second shell of an atom hold?

4. What is the atomic number equal to?

5. How does an atom make a positive ion?

6. When can sodium chloride conduct electricity?

7. Give **one** example of a molecule that has covalent bonds.

8. What is a group in the periodic table?

9. When sodium or potassium reacts with water, which gas does it give off?

10. Give the symbols for **three** elements in group 1.

11. Name **three** elements in the halogen group.

12. How many electrons are there in the outer shell of halogens?

13. What colour is bromine liquid?

14. What is the negative terminal in an electrolysis process called?

15. What types of ions are attracted to an anode?

16. What is the mineral that aluminium is extracted from called?

17. At which terminal is the aluminium deposited?

18. Give **three** reasons why gold is used in jewellery.

19. Describe the structure of a metal.

20. Describe how a metal conducts electricity.

Citizenship activity

Aluminium is very expensive to make.

A good deal of energy is needed to extract it.

QUESTIONS
1. Devise an advertising campaign to encourage the recycling of aluminium to save valuable resources.
   Your answer should include points about the:
   - damage that mining causes
   - cost of extracting minerals
   - energy costs
   - damage to the environment of using energy derived from fossil fuels
   - impact of litter from aluminium products
   - cost of separating and recycling aluminium
   - benefits of recycling aluminium.

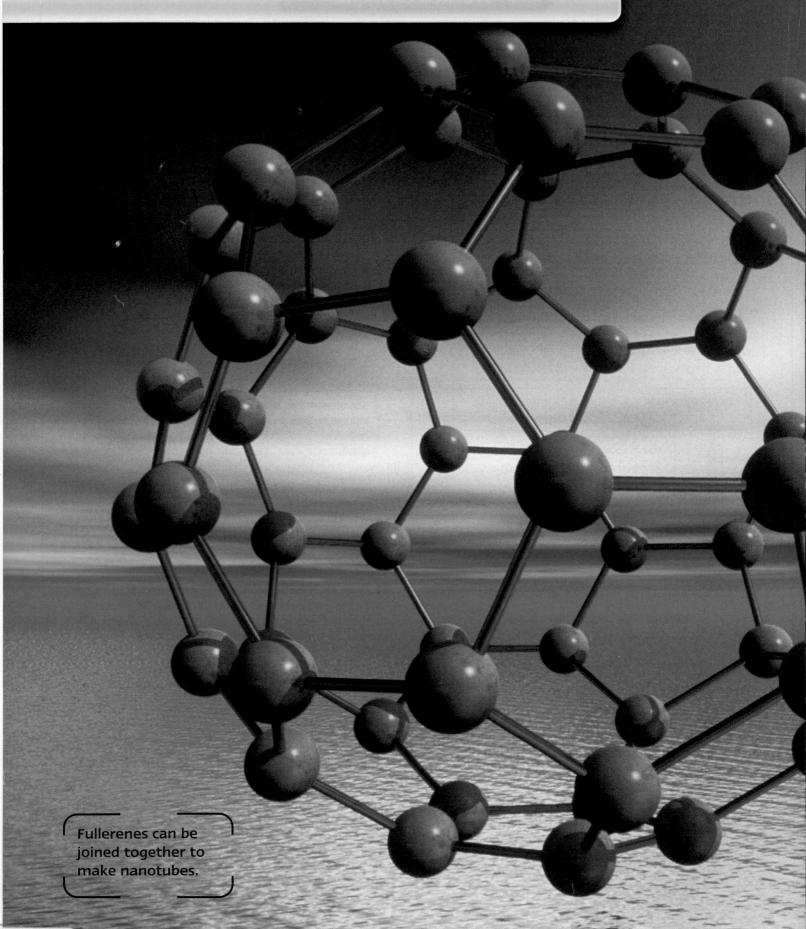

Fullerenes can be joined together to make nanotubes.

Buckminster fullerene is just one of the exciting new substances that scientists have recently discovered. It consists of the element carbon. The carbon atoms are joined together in pentagons and hexagons to form a perfect sphere. Scientists hope to use buckminster fullerene in cancer treatments and to target bacteria that have become resistant to antibiotics.

Fullerenes can be used to 'cage' other molecules. This is being used in new drug delivery systems.

Nanotubes can be used as semiconductors in electrical circuits, as industrial catalysts and to reinforce graphite in tennis rackets!

CONTENTS

Buckminster fullerene is a black solid made of 60 carbon atoms. It can be dissolved in petrol to form a deep red solution.

You will find out:

- about uses of sulfuric acid
- what a salt is
- how to predict which salts form when different acids react

Uses of sulfuric acid

Millions of tonnes of **sulfuric acid** are used every year. You probably only see sulfuric acid in the laboratory because in industry it is turned into other things.

Sulfuric acid is made into:

- fertilisers
- plastics
- paints
- explosives
- other chemicals.

Sulfuric acid is also used to clean metals. When metals **corrode** they form metal oxides, which are bases. The acid reacts with the metal oxide, taking away the corrosion.

FIGURE 2: Two uses of sulfuric acid: **a** these rolls of steel sheet are cleaned with sulfuric acid; **b** the liquid in a car battery is sulfuric acid.

FIGURE 3: Spot the sulfuric acid!

QUESTIONS

7 Describe **three** uses of sulfuric acid.

8 What does sulfuric acid react with when it 'cleans away' corrosion on metals?

...*balanced symbol equation*

More on acids and bases

Some common acids and bases are shown in the table.

Acid	Formula
hydrochloric acid	HCl
nitric acid	HNO_3
sulfuric acid	H_2SO_4
Base	
sodium hydroxide	NaOH
potassium hydroxide	KOH
ammonia solution (ammonium hydroxide)	NH_4OH
copper oxide	CuO
sodium carbonate	Na_2CO_3
calcium carbonate	$CaCO_3$

More on acid reactions

Reaction of acid with metal oxides or metal hydroxides

The reaction of a metal oxide or a metal hydroxide with an acid gives:

acid + oxide $\longrightarrow$ salt + water

acid + hydroxide $\longrightarrow$ salt + water

Reaction of acid with metal carbonates

The reaction of a metal carbonate with an acid is similar to that above, but a gas is also given off:

acid + carbonate $\longrightarrow$ salt + water + carbon dioxide

What is a salt?

A **salt** is made from part of a base and part of an acid. When sodium hydroxide reacts with hydrochloric acid, sodium chloride is formed.

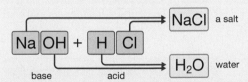

base   acid

To work out the name of a salt, look at the base and acid it was made from. Salt names have two parts, the first part from the base and the second part from the acid.

For example, when sodium hydroxide reacts with nitric acid, the salt formed is sodium nitrate:

sodium	nitrate
from the base	from the acid

- nitrates come from nitric acid
- chlorides come from hydrochloric acid
- sulfates come from sulfuric acid

Equations

The following are the **balanced symbol equations** for the reactions between some of the acids and bases listed above.

One acid reacts with one base

$HCl + NaOH \longrightarrow NaCl + H_2O$

$H_2SO_4 + CaCO_3 \longrightarrow CaSO_4 + H_2O + CO_2$

Two acids react with one base

$2HNO_3 + CuO \longrightarrow Cu[NO_3]_2 + H_2O$

$2HCl + CaCO_3 \longrightarrow CaCl_2 + H_2O + CO_2$

Two bases react with one acid

$H_2SO_4 + 2NaOH \longrightarrow Na_2SO_4 + 2H_2O$

QUESTIONS

9   What salt is formed when sulfuric acid reacts with copper oxide?

10   What salt is formed when nitric acid reacts with potassium hydroxide?

11   What salt is formed when hydrochloric acid reacts with magnesium carbonate?

12   What salt is formed when nitric acid reacts with calcium carbonate?

QUESTIONS

Write a balanced symbol equation for each of the following reactions.

13   HNO_3 and KOH.

14   HCl and CuO.

15   H_2SO_4 and NH_4OH.

Reacting masses

You will find out:

- about relative atomic mass
- how to work out relative formula mass

Weighty questions

Q. If an atom of hydrogen reacts with an atom of chlorine, why doesn't a gram of hydrogen react with a gram of chlorine?

A. Because different atoms weigh different amounts!

Element	Symbol	Relative atomic mass
hydrogen	H	1
carbon	C	12
nitrogen	N	14
oxygen	O	16
sulfur	S	32
chlorine	Cl	35.5

Relative atomic mass

Atoms of different elements weigh different amounts. We compare their **masses** using the **relative atomic mass** scale.

Hydrogen has a mass of 1 on this scale.

Other elements are heavier. For example, carbon has a relative atomic mass of 12.

Look at the **periodic table** on page 258 and find the relative atomic mass of some of the other elements.

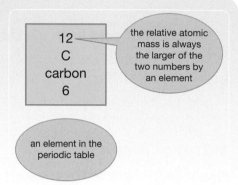

FIGURE 1: How to tell the relative atomic mass of carbon using the periodic table.

Relative formula mass

What if the atoms are combined?

Simply add up all the masses in the formula.

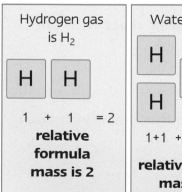

Hydrogen gas is H_2

$1 + 1 = 2$

relative formula mass is 2

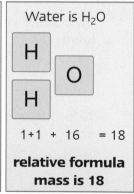

Water is H_2O

$1+1 + 16 = 18$

relative formula mass is 18

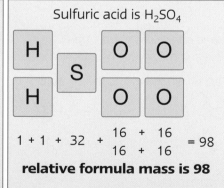

Sulfuric acid is H_2SO_4

$1 + 1 + 32 + \begin{array}{c} 16 + 16 \\ 16 + 16 \end{array} = 98$

relative formula mass is 98

EXAM HINTS AND TIPS

A relative mass is just a number. It doesn't have 'grams' after it.

QUESTIONS

You may need to use the periodic table on page 258 to help you to answer the following questions.

1 Lead, Pb, is a very dense metal. Find its relative atomic mass.
2 Uranium, U, is even more dense. Find its relative atomic mass.
3 Work out the relative formula mass of carbon dioxide, CO_2.
4 Work out the relative formula mass of propane, C_3H_8.

...mass   ...periodic table

More on relative formula masses

Relative formula masses are much more exciting when there are brackets to play with. They must be tackled in the right order!

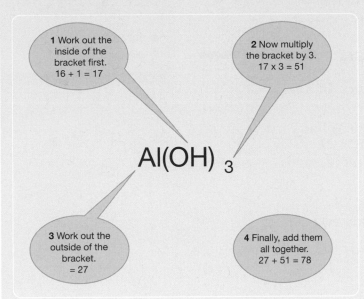

1 Work out the inside of the bracket first. 16 + 1 = 17

2 Now multiply the bracket by 3. 17 x 3 = 51

$Al(OH)_3$

3 Work out the outside of the bracket. = 27

4 Finally, add them all together. 27 + 51 = 78

The history of relative atomic mass

A relative mass is in fact a ratio, so there are no units.

Historically everything was compared to atoms of the lightest element, hydrogen. The relative atomic mass of an atom was the number of times it was heavier than hydrogen.

Everything is now compared to one-twelfth of an atom of carbon (which is effectively the same as comparing everything to hydrogen).

Copper sulfate 249.7 g

Iron (III) chloride 270.3 g

Potassium iodide 166.0 g

Potassium manganate (VII) 158.0 g

Sodium chloride 58.5 g

Cobalt nitrate 291.0 g

FIGURE 2: These compounds have different masses, but the amounts are the same.

QUESTIONS

5 Write down the relative formula masses of the following compounds.

a NH_4OH

b $Mg(OH)_2$

c $Mg(NO_3)_2$

d $Al_2(SO_4)_3$

QUESTIONS

6 Write down the relative formula masses of the following compounds.

a $(NH_4)_2SO_4$

b $(NH_4)_3PO_4$

c $(NH_4)_2Cr_2O_7$

What happens to the mass in a reaction?

The total mass in a reaction never changes.

In a reaction the mass of the **products** (chemicals at the end of the reaction) is exactly the same as the mass of the **reactants** (chemicals at the start of the reaction).

If the mass does seem to change, look for a reason.

- If the mass seems to go down, the reaction has probably given off a gas. Remember, gases do weigh something!
- If the mass seems to go up, a gas (probably oxygen) from the air has reacted with the chemical.

Yield and percentage yield

The **yield** of a reaction is the amount of chemical that is produced in the reaction.

The more reactant is used, the more product is made.

Sometimes a reaction does not seem to give as much chemical as it should. In real experiments, some chemicals always get left behind. The amount of product collected is usually less than the amount expected.

100% yield means that no product has been lost.
0% yield means that no product has been collected.

If all the lost bits of chemical could be collected, the total mass of product would be the same as the total mass of reactant.

How do bits of chemical get lost? Some ways are:

- loss in filtration – small amounts stay on the filter paper
- loss in evaporation – some chemicals evaporate into the room
- loss in transferring liquids – tiny amounts of liquid stick to the sides of the beaker and get left behind
- loss in heating – which makes things evaporate
- there might also be more than one reaction taking place – the reactants are being used up in a different reaction.

▌▌ QUESTIONS ▌▌

7   Joy makes a chemical by pouring two solutions into a beaker and then filtering off the solid.
    Suggest **two** reasons why the yield is less than 100%.

8   A reaction produces less than half the expected product. Choose the correct percentage yield from the list.
    30%   50%   70%   100%

...0% yield   ...100% yield

Simple calculations

You can work out how much product is produced in a reaction without knowing any chemical equations. Here are two useful methods.

Using conservation of mass

Q When calcium carbonate is heated it all turns into calcium oxide and carbon dioxide.
10 g of calcium carbonate produces 5.6 g of calcium oxide. How much carbon dioxide is made?

A If you start with 10 g of reactant, you must end up with 10 g of product. 5.6 g of product is calcium oxide, so 10 – 5.6 = 4.4 g carbon dioxide.

Using simple ratio

Q 2.4 g magnesium gives 4.0 g magnesium oxide. How much magnesium oxide will 4.8 g of magnesium make?

A Did you spot that the magnesium is twice as much? So it will make twice as much magnesium oxide, which is 8.0 g.

Calculating percentage yield

To calculate percentage yield the following two things must be known:

- the amount of product made, the 'actual yield'
- the amount of product that should have been made, the 'predicted yield'.

$$\text{percentage yield} = \frac{\text{actual yield}}{\text{predicted yield}} \times 100$$

Why is mass conserved?

When chemicals react, the atoms inside the reactants swap places to make new compounds – the products.

These products are made from just the same atoms as before. There are the same number of atoms at the end as there were at the start, so the overall mass stays the same.

Predicting the yield of a reaction

Predictions can be made by looking at the equation for a reaction.

example

$CaCO_3 \longrightarrow CaO + CO_2$

How much CO_2 is made when 500 g of $CaCO_3$ decompose?

Find the relative formula mass of $CaCO_3$.
40 + 12 + 16 + 16 + 16 = 100.

Now find the relative formula mass of CO_2.
12 + 16 + 16 = 44.

So 100 g $CaCO_3$ gives 44 g CO_2.

So 500 g $CaCO_3$ gives 5 × 44 = 220 g CO_2.

⬛⬛⬛ QUESTIONS ⬛⬛⬛

9 hydrogen + oxygen ⟶ water
32 g of oxygen reacted with hydrogen to make 36 g of water.
How much hydrogen was used?

10 32 g of copper made 40 g of copper oxide.
How much copper is needed to make 2 g of copper oxide?

11 Mohammed's reaction produces 48 g.
He had hoped for 64 g.
What is the percentage yield of his reaction?

⬛⬛⬛ QUESTIONS ⬛⬛⬛

12 $H_2 + Cl_2 \longrightarrow 2HCl$
How much HCl is made from 2 g of hydrogen?

13 The equation for burning propane is:
$C_3H_8 + 5O_2 \longrightarrow 3CO_2 + 4H_2O$
How much water is produced by 44 g of propane?

Fertilisers and crop yield

You will find out:

- about fertilisers and what they do
- about eutrophication
- how to calculate the percentages of elements in a fertiliser

Fertilisers make plants grOW!

Plants make most of their food from water and carbon dioxide in the air.

They make it by photosynthesising.

They only need small amounts of other elements, which their roots take from the soil.

Fertilisers give plants elements that may be in short supply in the soil.

Fertilisers increase crop yields.

Fertilisers

Carbon dioxide and water do not give a plant all the **elements** that it needs. The plant does still need tiny amounts of other elements. It gets these essential elements by taking in **minerals** through its roots.

Fertilisers help plants grow bigger and faster because they contain the essential elements plants need.

What are these essential elements? Three of the most important ones are:

- nitrogen, N
- phosphorus, P
- potassium, K.

Fertilisers that contain these elements are often called **NPK fertilisers**. The **formula** of a fertiliser gives the essential elements it contains. Just look for the symbols N, P and K.

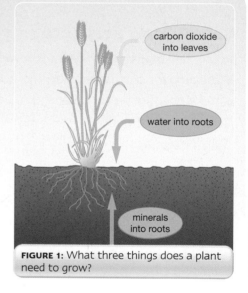

FIGURE 1: What three things does a plant need to grow?

carbon dioxide into leaves

water into roots

minerals into roots

FIGURE 2: How much N, P and K is there in these fertilisers?

QUESTIONS

1. Name the essential elements in potassium nitrate, KNO_3.
2. Name the essential elements in ammonium phosphate.

...*crop yield* ...*element* ...*eutrophication* ...*fertiliser* ...*formula*

More on fertilisers

Farmers use fertilisers to increase their **crop yields**. This gives them more grains of wheat, larger grains of wheat, or both.

Even though plants need certain essential elements, it is no use putting them into the soil as pure elements. They have to be turned into chemical compounds first. The plants absorb these compounds through their roots. They can only do this if the compounds dissolve in water. Most fertilisers dissolve easily, but some dissolve slowly – so that the chemicals are let out into the soil over a long time period.

Relative formula mass of fertilisers

To get the most out of a fertiliser its **relative formula mass** needs to be calculated.

example

Use the periodic table on page 258 to help you with this example. The relative formula mass of ammonium nitrate is:

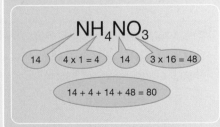

NH_4NO_3

14   4 x 1 = 4   14   3 x 16 = 48

14 + 4 + 14 + 48 = 80

QUESTIONS

3 What are the relative formula masses of:

a potassium nitrate, KNO_3?

b ammonium sulfate, $(NH_4)_2SO_4$?

Why farmers use fertilisers

Plants normally grow well in ordinary soil. The chemicals that the plants need are already dissolved in the soil water. However, a farmer's crop may well need more dissolved minerals than are present in the soil. When crops are grown in a field year after year the minerals are gradually removed by the plants. It takes time for more of the essential elements to dissolve. The farmer uses fertiliser to put back the missing essential elements into the soil quickly.

Nitrogen is especially important to plants. **Proteins** are essential for growth, and protein molecules all contain nitrogen atoms. If a plant gets more nitrogen it makes more protein, so it can grow more.

What is the percentage of an essential element in a fertiliser?

Farmers can use relative formula masses to find the percentage of each element in a fertiliser – it is even printed on the bag for them.

$$\text{percentage of element} = \frac{\text{mass of the element in the formula} \times 100}{\text{relative formula mass}}$$

example

Calculate the percentage of nitrogen in ammonium nitrate, NH_4NO_3.

The relative formula mass of NH_4NO_3 is $14 + 4 + 14 + (16 \times 3) = 80$.

There are two nitrogens in the formula (one in the ammonium and one in the nitrate) so the mass of nitrogen = 28.

The percentage that is nitrogen is $\dfrac{28 \times 100}{80} = 35\%$.

Fertilisers in the wrong place – eutrophication

Fertilisers must be applied carefully. Rain water dissolves fertilisers which run off into nearby water courses. When the level of fertilisers in a water course rises too high **eutrophication** occurs.

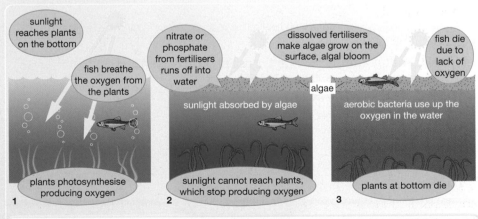

FIGURE 3: Eutrophication. What causes eutrophication?

QUESTIONS

4 Suggest why ammonium nitrate makes such a useful fertiliser.

5 Why might a farmer use potassium nitrate instead of ammonium nitrate as a fertiliser for his crops?

Making fertilisers

Fertilisers can be made by **neutralising** alkalis with acids.

You will find out:
- how a fertiliser is made from an acid and an alkali
- the names of some nitrogenous fertilisers

1   Use a measuring cylinder to pour alkali into a conical flask.

2   Add acid to the alkali until it is neutral.

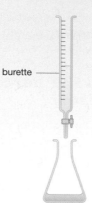

measuring cylinder

conical flask

burette

3   Evaporate.

4   Filter off the crystals.

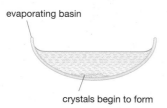

evaporating basin

crystals begin to form

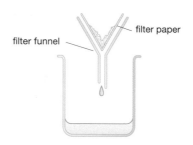

filter paper

filter funnel

FIGURE 4: Making a fertiliser using a neutralisation reaction. Why is the solution filtered?

A fertiliser that contains nitrogen is called a **nitrogenous** fertiliser.

Here are the names of some nitrogenous fertilisers:

- ammonium nitrate
- ammonium phosphate
- ammonium sulfate
- urea.

EXAM HINTS AND TIPS

You need to know the names of these nitrogenous fertilisers!

QUESTIONS

6   What does a nitrogenous fertiliser contain?

7   Which of the following are nitrogenous fertilisers?

**ammonium sulfate   potassium chlorate
potassium nitrate   sodium sulfate**

8   Ammonium sulfate is a nitrogenous fertiliser. Which part of the name tells you that it contains nitrogen?

...*indicator* ...*neutralise*

More on making fertilisers

Many fertilisers are **salts**, so they can be made by reacting acids with bases.

> acid   +   base   ⟶   salt   +   water

Which acids and bases make which fertilisers?

> nitric acid   +   potassium hydroxide   ⟶   potassium nitrate   +   water

> nitric acid   +   ammonium hydroxide   ⟶   ammonium nitrate   +   water

> sulfuric acid   +   ammonium hydroxide   ⟶   ammonium sulfate   +   water

> phosphoric acid   +   ammonium hydroxide   ⟶   ammonium phosphate   +   water

Making ammonium sulfate in the laboratory

React sulfuric acid (acid) with ammonium hydroxide (base).

> sulfuric acid   +   ammonium hydroxide   ⟶   ammonium sulfate   +   water

The amounts used in the reaction must be exactly right. If too much acid or too much base is used the plants will be killed. To find out exactly how much to use, a **titration** is carried out before mixing the main batch of chemicals.

Method

- Titrate the alkali with the acid, using an **indicator**.
- Repeat the titration until consistent results are obtained.

The acid and alkali have now reacted completely. This makes a neutral solution of potassium nitrate fertiliser, but the fertiliser is contaminated with indicator.

- Use the titration result to add the correct amounts of acid and alkali together without the indicator.
- The fertiliser you have made is dissolved in water, so evaporate most of the water using a hot water bath.
- Leave the remaining solution to crystallise.
- Filter off the crystals.

FIGURE 5: Carrying out a titration in the laboratory. How can the end point of a titration be detected?

QUESTIONS

9 Which acid and base react to make ammonium sulfate?

10 Which acid and base react to make potassium nitrate?

11 What substance is produced when nitric acid reacts with ammonium hydroxide?

12 What substance is produced when phosphoric acid reacts with ammonium hydroxide?

QUESTIONS

13 Suggest how a solid sample of ammonium phosphate could be made. Outline all the main stages.

...nitrogenous ...salt ...titration

Making ammonia — Haber process and costs

You will find out:
- how ammonia is made
- about reversible reactions
- why special conditions are used in the manufacture of ammonia

'Ammonia is the key to reducing starvation'

About 100 years ago people found out how to make ammonia from the air.

Since then, the use of ammonia-based fertilisers on crops has stopped millions of people from starving.

The number of starving people in the world has fallen due to the use of fertilisers.

> **DID YOU KNOW?**
> A factory that makes chemicals is called a 'plant'. So an ammonia plant makes fertilisers for plants to grow!

Ammonia

The **formula** for **ammonia** is NH_3. Ammonia is made by joining **nitrogen** and **hydrogen**.

Nitrogen comes from air. Hydrogen is made from natural gas or by **cracking** oil fractions.

Nitrogen is **unreactive**, but in 1908 Fritz **Haber** found that he could make nitrogen react with hydrogen if he used an iron **catalyst**. Haber's discovery is now used to make millions of tonnes of ammonia every year.

Haber's process has two reactions.

- A forward reaction.

$$\boxed{\text{nitrogen + hydrogen}} \longrightarrow \boxed{\text{ammonia}}$$

- A backward reaction.

$$\boxed{\text{nitrogen + hydrogen}} \longleftarrow \boxed{\text{ammonia}}$$

The reaction goes in both directions – at the same time!

Reactions that go in both directions are called **reversible reactions**.

To write an equation for a reversible reaction we use a special arrow, $\rightleftharpoons$, to show that the reaction goes both ways.

$$\text{nitrogen + hydrogen} \rightleftharpoons \text{ammonia}$$

> **QUESTIONS**
> 1 Give **two** features of a catalyst.
> 2 Write a word equation for the reaction between nitrogen and hydrogen.
> 3 What does the symbol $\rightleftharpoons$ mean?
> 4 Fritz Haber solved the problem of making nitrogen and hydrogen react. What was the problem?

> **DID YOU KNOW?**
> A catalyst is something which speeds up a reaction, and can be recovered at the end of the reaction.

...ammonia ...catalyst ...cracking ...efficient ...formula ...Haber ...hydrogen

The Haber process

nitrogen + hydrogen ⇌ ammonia

Every bit of grain crop grown in the world needs nitrogen. Over half of that nitrogen comes from man-made fertilisers! The only way these fertilisers can be made starts with the Haber process.

Ammonia manufacture has to be **efficient** to produce large quantities. To work most efficiently the Haber process uses:

- an iron catalyst
- high pressure
- a temperature of around 450 °C
- a recycling system. Not all the nitrogen and hydrogen react, so the nitrogen and hydrogen that do not react are sent back into the reaction vessel.

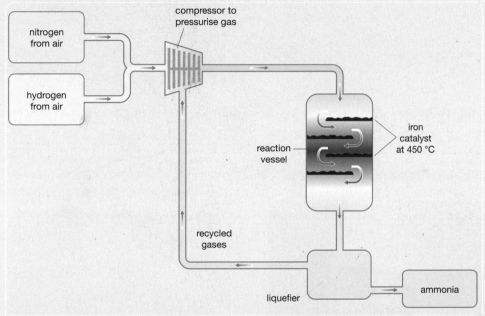

FIGURE 1: The Haber process. Suggest how the compressor helps to make the reaction more efficient.

More on the Haber process

$N_2 + 3H_2 \rightleftharpoons 2NH_3$

As the reaction is reversible, the **percentage yield** for the reaction cannot be 100 per cent. Surprisingly the conditions inside the Haber plant do not even give as high a percentage yield as they could.

- The high pressure increases the percentage yield – but even higher pressures could be used.
- The high temperature decreases the percentage yield. However, high temperatures do make the reaction go faster.
- 450 °C is an **optimum temperature** – the yield is not as good, but that yield is made faster, so that more is produced.
- Catalysts do not affect the yield – they just make the reaction go faster.

QUESTIONS

5 What is ammonia made from?

6 Write down the **four** important conditions used in the industrial manufacture of ammonia.

7 What happens when hydrogen and nitrogen are passed over an iron catalyst?

QUESTIONS

8 Ammonia can be removed by cooling the gases coming out of the reaction vessel. Explain why cooling the gases which are to be recycled increases energy consumption.

You will find out:
- what affects the costs of making a chemical

What affects the costs of running a big chemical plant?

Modern ammonia plants make 1500 tonnes of ammonia every day. These plants are carefully designed to keep the cost of making ammonia as low as possible.

What affects the cost of making ammonia?

- The cost of building the plant in the first place.
- The labour costs – paying people's wages.
- The cost of the chemicals – the hydrogen and nitrogen.
- The energy costs.
- How fast the reaction will go – the catalyst makes it go faster, so more ammonia can be made.

What is ammonia used for?

When Fritz Haber first did his experiments, he wanted the ammonia to make explosives.

These days:

- over 80 per cent of all ammonia goes into fertilisers
- ammonia is also used to make nitric acid – most of which goes into more fertilisers
- very small amounts of ammonia are used to make household cleaners.

FIGURE 2: Uses of ammonia: **a** fertilisers; **b** ammonia-based cleaning products.

◼◼ QUESTIONS ◼◼

9 What is the main use of ammonia?

10 What would happen to the costs if ammonia could be made at a lower temperature?
Explain your answer.

...fuel   ...optimum conditions

What affects the costs of ammonia production?

- Labour costs. Many chemical plants are now heavily automated and they need very few people to operate them.

- The cost of the reactants. Hydrogen is made from natural gas or by cracking oil fractions, which costs money. Nitrogen comes from the air but it is not free! It has to be cleaned, dried and compressed.

- Recycling unreacted materials means that money is not wasted on unused reactants.

- High pressure makes the reaction work better, but costs more. The pipes and fittings have to be made of stronger steel. Designers use a pressure that gives a good yield but which does not make it impossibly expensive to make the equipment.

FIGURE 3: A chemical plant. Can you list the factors that affect the cost of producing ammonia?

- There are energy costs – the higher the temperature, the more **fuel** is needed.

- How fast the reaction goes. The faster the reaction, the more product is made from the same equipment, so the cheaper it is. Chemists are always trying to improve the catalyst so that the reaction will go even faster.

- **Pollution** control costs. Reducing pollution is expensive and manufacturers have always tried to make their chemicals as cheaply as possible. Anti-pollution laws now mean that the chemicals cost a little bit more, but the plants do much less damage to the environment.

Optimum conditions

Chemical plants do not work at the conditions that produce the highest percentage yield for a reaction. They work at the conditions that will make the chemical most cheaply. These are known as the **optimum conditions**.

Temperature is especially important. High temperature should be bad for this reaction, yet it runs at 450 °C. This sort of temperature means higher energy costs and also lower yields. However, the increase in **rate** more than compensates; the plant produces more ammonia in a day at this temperature than it would at lower, more 'efficient' temperatures.

The reaction has a low percentage yield. However, as long as the unreacted chemicals can be recycled, they can go back into the reaction vessel. It is the combination of yield and rate that must give enough product.

Total energy costs are not solely due to heating costs. The plant needs compressors and pumps to achieve a high pressure and to move chemicals through pipes.

QUESTIONS

Pressure in atmospheres	Temperature			
	100 °C	200 °C	300 °C	400 °C
50	95%	74%	40%	15%
100	97%	82%	53%	25%
200	99%	89%	67%	39%

Yield of ammonia at different temperatures and pressures

11 What conditions in the table give the lowest yield of ammonia?

12 What conditions in the table give the highest yield of ammonia? Explain why these conditions are not used.

QUESTIONS

13 Haber plants are often built next to oil refineries. Explain why this reduces costs.

14 Many chemists have tried to find new catalysts that would make the Haber process operate more quickly. Suggest **two** ways in which the costs would be less if a Haber plant could be built with better catalysts.

Fighting a war with chemicals

SELF-CHECK ACTIVITY

STEP 1

Guano is a huge natural source of ammonia. Why did Germany want to be independent of the guano deposits in Chile? You may be able to give a better answer if you find the two countries on a map.

CONTEXT

Fritz Haber's name is associated with the Haber process used to make ammonia. Haber was born in 1868 in Prussia – a part of Europe that was to become Germany.

Ammonia was important to Germany (and to many other countries) for two reasons – it is used to make fertilisers and explosives. When Haber started looking at the supply of ammonia, the industry was already well established but relied on a natural source – bird droppings. In Chile, South America, there was one of the world's largest deposits of bird droppings. It was about 220 miles long and over 1.5 metres thick! The deposits are called guano.

Haber, together with another German scientist, Carl Bosch, developed a way of manufacturing ammonia. Ammonia has the formula NH_3 and they came up with a way of making it from nitrogen and hydrogen, at conditions of high temperature and pressure and with an iron catalyst.

At the outbreak of World War I, Haber placed himself and his team of scientists at the service of the German government. His development of ammonia production meant that Germany could produce large quantities of explosives for the war effort and undoubtedly helped to increase its effectiveness as a fighting force. Haber also developed methods of chemical warfare and he organised and directed the use of chlorine gas at Ypres in 1915, which killed thousands of Allied troops and hundreds of German troops as well.

Germany lost the war in 1918, but in that year Haber was awarded the Nobel prize for his work on the synthesis of ammonia. There was criticism of him though in the scientific community because of his willingness to use his skills in developing weapons of war.

Why is it true that ammonia has the ability to sustain life and to destroy it?

Do some research on nitrogen and explain why it is not surprising that ammonia synthesis needs a very high temperature and pressure.

Iron has the symbol Fe. If iron is needed in the synthesis of ammonia, why does Fe not appear in the formula for ammonia?

Guano deposits provide a natural source of ammonia.

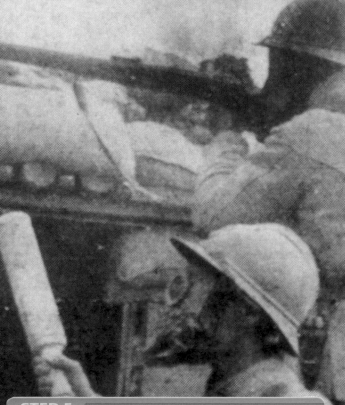

Maximise your grade

These sentences show what you need to be including in your work. Use these to improve your work and to be successful.

Grade	Answer includes...
F	State **one** beneficial use of ammonia and **one** harmful use.
	State, using information found from a map, why Germany did not want to import guano from Chile.
	State **one** reason why some scientists approved of Haber receiving the Nobel Prize.
	Explain the term 'catalyst' and state the chemical used as a catalyst in the Haber process.
C	Write a word equation for the formation of ammonia by the Haber process. Explain what is meant by 'reversible reaction'.
	Explain why some scientists did not approve of Haber receiving the Nobel Prize. Suggest a reason for him leaving Germany in 1933.
A	Explain reasons why the Haber process takes place at high temperatures and at high pressures.
	Explain, in terms of pressure and temperature, what is meant by 'optimum conditions'.

In the period following World War I, Haber received recognition at the highest level for his work on ammonia synthesis, but was criticised by many other scientists in the international community. Explain why opinions about him varied.

Detergents

You will find out:
- what is in washing powders
- why clothes are washed at low temperatures
- how soap gets dirt off clothes

How clean can we go?

Manufacturers tell us that their washing powders wash 'whiter than white'. This is not just hype – they really do. There is a huge amount of science inside a box of washing powder!

What is in a box of washing powder?

There is more in washing powder than just soap. Here are some things that might be in it.

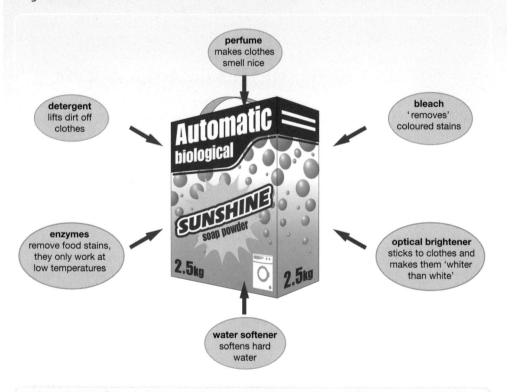

perfume
makes clothes
smell nice

detergent
lifts dirt off
clothes

bleach
'removes'
coloured stains

enzymes
remove food stains,
they only work at
low temperatures

optical brightener
sticks to clothes and
makes them 'whiter
than white'

water softener
softens hard
water

DID YOU KNOW?

An average load of washing has 40 g of dirt. That is about three large spoonfuls. Very dirty washing has a lot more!

DID YOU KNOW?

Bleach doesn't remove stains; it just turns them colourless so that they can't be seen.

FIGURE 1: Some of the things in washing powder. What do enzymes do?

There are different types of **detergent**; soap is just one of them. Many detergents are also **salts**.

QUESTIONS

1 List **five** things in a soap powder.
2 Washing powders that have enzymes in them must only be used at low temperatures. Find out why.

...acid   ...detergent   ...hydrophilic

What are detergents?

Detergents can be made by **neutralising** some organic **acids** with alkali.

acid + alkali ⟶ salt + water

The salt is the detergent. It is suitable for cleaning uses because:
- it dissolves grease stains
- it dissolves in water.

Once the detergent has dissolved the grease, it lifts the grease stain off into the water.

Why are clothes washed at low temperatures?

It is good for the environment to wash clothes at 40 °C instead of at high temperatures. Why is this?

Washing machines have to heat up a lot of water. This needs energy, so the lower the temperature of the water the less energy is used and the less greenhouse gases are put into the atmosphere.

Washing clothes at low temperatures is also good for coloured clothes – many dyes are easily damaged by high temperatures.

How does a detergent work?

When clothes are washed, dirt is lifted off the clothes and put into water. If the dirt dissolves in water, this is easy. If the dirt is made from oil or grease it will not dissolve in water. Detergents help by dissolving the grease.

A detergent molecule is made from two parts: one part dissolves in oil and grease (the **hydrophobic** part) and the other part dissolves in water (the **hydrophilic** part).

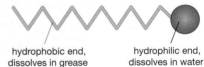

hydrophobic end, dissolves in grease

hydrophilic end, dissolves in water

FIGURE 2: A detergent molecule. Why do we use detergents to help to clean clothes?

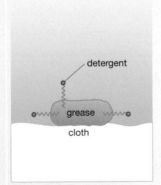

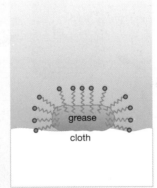

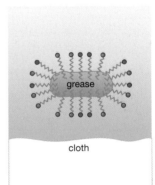

1 The hydrophobic (water hating) ends of detergent molecules start to dissolve in the grease. This leaves the hydrophilic (water soluble) ends on the outside.

2 Eventually, so many detergent molecules are stuck to the grease that the outside of the grease is covered in water soluble ends.

3 The grease now dissolves in the water and floats away.

FIGURE 3: How a detergent works.

QUESTIONS

3 Explain why lower wash temperatures result in lower emissions of greenhouse gases.

4 Suggest the name of the salt formed when stearic acid reacts with potassium hydroxide.

QUESTIONS

5 Give **two** reasons why clothes should be rinsed after they have been washed.

6 The chemical name for one type of soap is sodium oleate.

　a Suggest the name of the alkali which could be used to make it.

　b Suggest the name of the acid that the soap is based on.

Solvents and solutes

Fresh coffee stains dissolve in water but Biro marks do not. However, Biro marks will often dissolve in methylated spirit. Methylated spirit and water are both **solvents** – they dissolve other substances. A substance that dissolves in a solvent is a **solute**. Biro ink dissolved in a solvent makes a **solution**.

Different solvents dissolve different substances. If a substance dissolves, it is **soluble**. If it does not dissolve, it is **insoluble**.

What is in a bottle of washing up liquid?

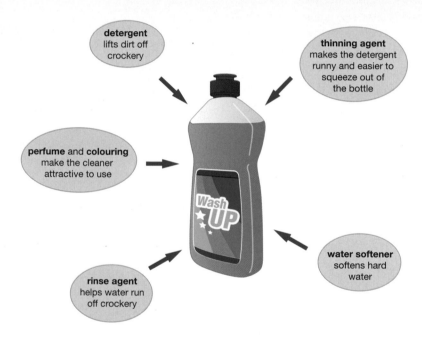

detergent
lifts dirt off crockery

thinning agent
makes the detergent runny and easier to squeeze out of the bottle

perfume and **colouring**
make the cleaner attractive to use

water softener
softens hard water

rinse agent
helps water run off crockery

FIGURE 4: Some of the things in washing up liquid. What does rinse agent do?

You will find out:

- how dry cleaning works
- the link between detergents, acids and alkalis

QUESTIONS

7 David makes a cup of tea and adds some sugar to it.

   a What is the solute that he has used?

   b What is the solvent?

8 Write down the names of **three** different solvents.

9 Name **one** substance that is in washing up liquid but not in soap powder.

...dry clean   ...hydrogen bond   ...insoluble   ...intermolecular force

How does dry cleaning work?

Molecules stick to each other. They are held together by weak forces of attraction. Forces between molecules are called **intermolecular forces**. They are different from the chemical bonds that hold the atoms inside a molecule together.

Molecules of grease are held together by weak intermolecular forces. The same type of forces hold molecules of dry-cleaning solvent together.

The forces join anything to anything, so dry-cleaning solvent molecules also bind to grease. The grease then dissolves in the solvent.

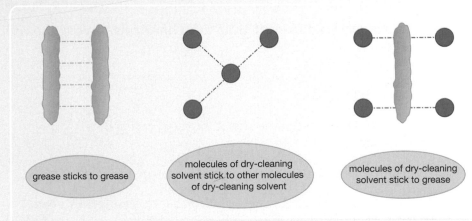

grease sticks to grease

molecules of dry-cleaning solvent stick to other molecules of dry-cleaning solvent

molecules of dry-cleaning solvent stick to grease

FIGURE 5: Dry-cleaning solvent molecules stick to grease as happily as they stick to each other. How does this make the solvent a good cleaning agent?

Molecules of water are held together by stronger intermolecular forces called **hydrogen bonds**.

The water molecules cannot stick to the grease because they are sticking to each other much too strongly.

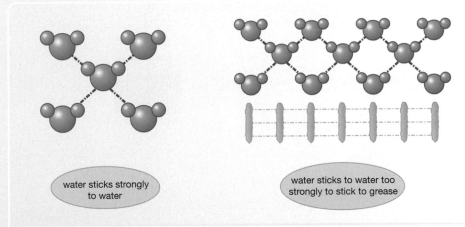

water sticks strongly to water

water sticks to water too strongly to stick to grease

FIGURE 6: Water molecules are held tightly together and do not stick to grease molecules.

Dry cleaning

Some fabrics will be damaged if they are washed in water – they must be **dry cleaned**. A dry-cleaning machine washes clothes in an organic solvent. The 'dry' does not mean that no liquids are used, just that the liquid is not water.

Most of the stains on clothing contain grease from the skin or from food. Grease-based stains do not dissolve in water, but they do dissolve easily in a dry-cleaning solvent.

QUESTIONS

10 What does the 'dry' in dry cleaning mean?

11 Dry cleaning removes grease stains better than water. Explain why.

QUESTIONS

12 When a washing machine washes clothes in water it spins the clothes to remove most of the water. The clothes are then hung out to dry to let the remaining water evaporate. Dry cleaning uses a more complicated spin cycle because the clothes are not hung out.
Suggest why clothes are not hung out to dry in dry cleaning.

Batch or continuous?

You will find out:
- about the differences between batch and continuous processes

How are chemicals made?

An ammonia plant makes thousands of tonnes of ammonia every day.

A drugs company may make less than a tonne of a medicine in a whole year.

These amounts are so different that the chemicals have to be made in very different ways.

Continuous process

If something is needed in large amounts it is usually made by a **continuous process**.

For example, ammonia is made by a continuous process.

Nitrogen and hydrogen are continuously pumped into a **reaction vessel** and ammonia is made all the time.

The reaction vessel never stops; it works night and day throughout the year.

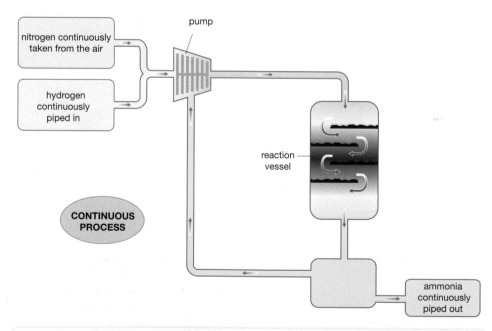

FIGURE 1: A continuous process is used to make ammonia. Can you describe why the process is continuous?

DID YOU KNOW?

Wrapped bread is cooked by a continuous process. The bread sits on a slow-moving conveyor belt through a very long oven.

QUESTIONS

1 Name **one** substance that is made by a batch process.
2 Name **one** substance that is made by a continuous process.

...batch process ...continuous process

Batch process

If a chemical is needed in small amounts it is made by a **batch process**.

Drugs companies make most medicines in small amounts – batches – and then store the medicines in a warehouse. New batches are then made whenever the stored medicine runs low.

Once they have made a batch of one drug it is easy to switch to making a different drug.

If a lot of one medicine is needed, several batches can be made at the same time.

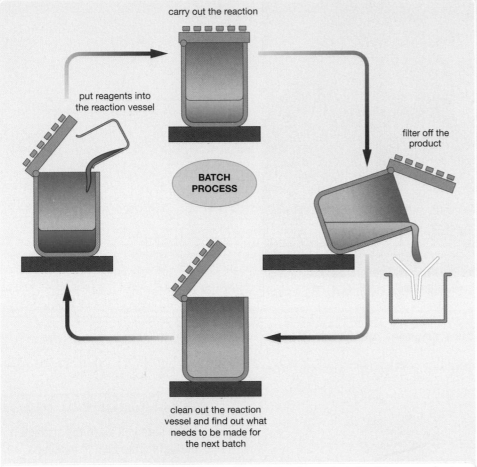

carry out the reaction

put reagents into the reaction vessel

BATCH PROCESS

filter off the product

clean out the reaction vessel and find out what needs to be made for the next batch

FIGURE 2: A batch process is used to make small amounts of a product. Medicines are often made in this way. Can you suggest why?

3　The local baker makes her bread in a batch process. Suggest the main stages in making a batch of bread.

4　The local baker makes batches of different 'product' every day. Suggest what the different batches might be.

Continuous process

A continuous process **plant** is effective because it works at full capacity all the time. It costs an enormous amount to build, but once running it makes a large amount of product and employs very few people, making the cost per tonne very small.

A disadvantage is that the reaction vessels and pipes are only designed to work well at one level of output. What they make or how much cannot easily be changed.

Batch process

Batch processes, by comparison, are flexible. It is easy to change from making one compound to another. Each batch has to be supervised, so labour costs are higher. Also, time spent filling and emptying reaction vessels is time when the vessels are not producing chemicals, so they are not used as efficiently as in a continuous process.

FIGURE 3: A medicine being made by batch process. What are the disadvantages of a batch process?

5　Suggest how running a continuous process plant at a slower rate increases the running costs.

6　Someone discovers a way of making ammonia from domestic rubbish. Suggest how this would affect Haber plants.

Factors affecting the costs of medicines

Sometimes the **raw materials** for a medicine are extracted from plants.

You will find out:

- about factors that affect the cost of making drugs
- how some chemicals can be extracted from plants

FIGURE 4: The foxglove plant gives the heart medicine called digitalis.

Other medicines are made totally in the laboratory; they are **synthetic**.

Whichever way the medicines are made, there are costs.

EXAM HINTS AND TIPS

Make sure you learn the six factors that affect the cost of making a medicine.

labour costs

research and testing

energy costs

DRUG COST

raw materials

time for development

marketing, legal costs

FIGURE 5: Six factors that affect the cost of making a medicine.

QUESTIONS

7 List **six** factors that affect the cost of making a medicine.

8 Why are some flowering plants important to drugs companies?

...chromatography ...development ...generic

Why are medicines so expensive?

- It can take many years to develop a new medicine, and even longer to test its safety. Each country has strict safety laws to guide drugs companies. The price for a new medicine is set so that the investment costs of its research and development can be recouped.

- The raw materials needed to make a medicine may be rare and costly. The medicine may be based on compounds extracted from plants that are difficult to find. We sometimes have to go to the far ends of the Earth to get them.

- Raw materials are sometimes difficult to extract. A flowering plant may contain thousands of similar chemicals, so separating the desired chemical is time consuming and expensive.

- Medicines are made by batch processes, so less automation can be used and their manufacture is labour intensive.

Extracting chemicals from plants

Chemical compounds in a plant are held in its cells. Plant cells have tough walls, so to extract the compound the plant is crushed to break the cell walls. Then the chemical must be dissolved. This only works if a suitable solvent is used. The solvent dissolves lots of different compounds, so the desired compound is then separated from the others. This can be done by **chromatography**.

FIGURE 6: Chromatography on an industrial scale. What is chromatography used for?

Drug development

The price of a drug has to reflect more than the cost of finding the chemicals and getting them to react.

- Drug **development** is expensive. Promising compounds often have dangerous side-effects. The company then has to make lots of similar compounds to find the one with the fewest side-effects. Tests on as many as 10 000 compounds can be made before an effective one is found.

- A new drug must be tested for safety and submitted for approval. It may take 4 years to develop a drug and then a further 10 years to test it and gain approval. Only then can it start earning money to pay for the staff costs during its development.

- The company **patents** the drug, so for the next 20 years or so they can sell it for a high price. The drugs company has to recoup all of its development costs in that time, because after that other companies can make their version of the same drug. These are called **generic** drugs. The price for generic drugs is much lower as they have no initial development cost.

- If the new drug is wanted in developed countries, then the company knows that it can sell a lot and get its money back easily. If it is mainly needed in very poor countries that cannot afford it, the company will find it much harder to cover its costs.

QUESTIONS

11 Explain why generic drugs have no initial development costs.

12 Suggest why a drugs company has to submit a new drug for approval before it is sold.

13 Suggest why it takes so long to test the safety of a drug.

QUESTIONS

9 List the main processes in extracting a chemical from a plant.

10 What is meant when it is said that chromatography can 'purify' a chemical compound?

...patent ...raw material ...synthetic

Nanochemistry

You will find out:

- about the properties of diamonds
- how to recognise the structures of diamond, graphite and buckminster fullerene
- about allotropes

At the cutting edge

Soot and diamonds are formed from carbon.

Pencil leads are also a form of carbon, called graphite.

And so is buckminster fullerene. (Have you even heard of it?)

They are all the same element, carbon. The reasons for the differences are at the 'nano' level – the level where atoms fit together.

What does a diamond look like?

Diamond is made from **carbon**. The main uses of diamonds are as cutting tools and in jewellery.

We all know what a diamond looks like, but what words are used to describe it?

Gem-quality diamonds:

- are clear (transparent), colourless and **lustrous**
- have a high melting point
- are insoluble in water
- do not conduct electricity
- are hard.

Industrial diamonds are nowhere near as pretty. They are often **opaque** and dark brown or black. But they have all the other properties, especially hardness!

FIGURE 1: Industrial diamonds. What is the difference between jewellery diamonds and industrial diamonds?

QUESTIONS

1. Name the element that diamonds are made from.
2. Give **six** properties of gem-quality diamonds.

...allotrope ...carbon ...covalent bond ...diamond

How can carbon atoms be arranged?

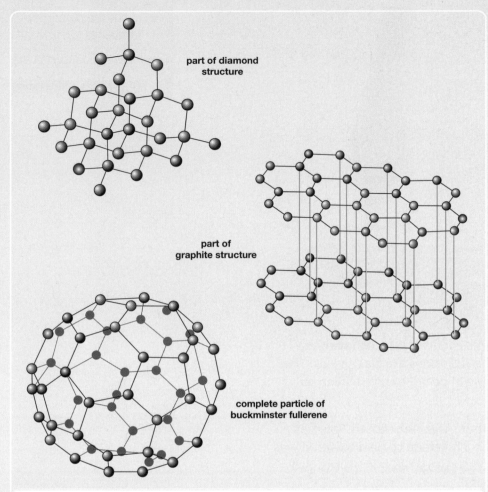

part of diamond
structure

part of
graphite structure

complete particle of
buckminster fullerene

FIGURE 2: Carbon atoms can arrange in three different ways. What do you notice about the bonds between the layers of atoms in graphite?

Diamonds are the hardest natural substance known. Diamonds also have a very high melting point. These properties make them ideal for industrial cutting tools, such as rock saws and grinding wheels.

Gem diamonds are lustrous (the way they reflect light). They are often thought of as colourless, but in fact gem diamonds do have slight colour. Industrial diamonds, being impure, are often strongly coloured and **opaque**.

Allotropes

Different arrangements of the atoms inside an element can result in different structures. These different forms of the same element are called **allotropes**. Diamond, graphite and the fullerenes are all allotropes of carbon.

These different arrangements of atoms give each allotrope different properties.

In diamond, each atom is held by **covalent bonds** to four other atoms, which are bonded to more, which are bonded to more, and so on. This is called a **giant structure**. The covalent bonds are strong, so it is very difficult to melt a giant structure – all the bonds need to break at once.

The bonding in diamond is also responsible for its hardness. The atoms are not only held strongly, they can also resist forces from any direction. Look at the diagram of diamond – the bonds are **tetrahedrally** arranged. This is the strongest possible configuration.

▨▨▨ QUESTIONS ▨▨▨

3 Suggest why a high melting point is important for the blades of industrial cutting tools.

4 Name the **three** forms of carbon.

▨▨▨ QUESTIONS ▨▨▨

5 Buckminster fullerene has a lower melting and boiling point than diamond. Use your knowledge of their structures to explain why.

Graphite

Graphite is made from carbon, just like diamond, but it is very different.

- Unlike gem diamonds, graphite is black and opaque, though it is still lustrous.
- Graphite is soft and feels slippery. It is so slippery that it is used as a **lubricant** and in pencil leads.
- Like diamond, it does not dissolve in water, but unlike diamond it conducts electricity well. Graphite conducts electricity so well that electrodes are made from it.

FIGURE 3: Pencil leads are made from graphite. What properties of graphite make it good for use in pencils?

You will find out:

- about the properties of graphite
- about the properties of fullerenes
- what nanoparticles are

Fullerenes

There is a third way of putting carbon atoms together, the **fullerenes**. Discovered just a few years ago in 1985, the fullerenes are black solids. They do not dissolve in water, but they do dissolve in petrol to give a deep red solution.

Fullerenes are tiny particles made from carbon. The particles are so small that they are called **nanoparticles**. The first fullerene to be discovered was named **buckminster fullerene**. It is a hollow ball of carbon atoms. Balls of atoms like this are often called 'bucky balls'.

Scientists then learnt to make hollow tubes of carbon atoms. These are called **nanotubes**, or sometimes bucky tubes. Nanotubes are very strong and conduct electricity.

Nanochemistry

Chemistry normally works on a large scale. When we think of chemistry we think of reactions in a chemical works and in test tubes. Even a test tube holds billions and billions of particles. With bucky balls and nanotubes, scientists are dealing with individual particles. This is called working at the **nanoscale** (at the level of atoms).

▦ QUESTIONS ▦

6 List the similarities between diamond and graphite.

7 List the differences between diamond and graphite.

8 Chemicals are used on three levels of scale: industrial, test tube and the nano level.
   Give **one** example of each level.

...buckminster fullerene   ...bulk properties   ...delocalised   ...fullerene   ...graphite

Graphite

Pencils contain graphite, which is black and slippery. When a pencil is used, some of the graphite slides off and sticks to the paper, making black marks. The slipperiness also makes graphite a good lubricant, even though it is a solid. Powdered graphite is often used to lubricate door locks.

Graphite conducts electricity. This is unusual – this form of carbon is the only non-metal element that can conduct. The graphite is often used for electrodes in electrolysis. As it has a high melting point, it can be used to electrolyse molten compounds at high temperatures.

Fullerenes

When the first fullerene was discovered, scientists realised that it was exactly the same shape as the geodesic domes built by an architect called Buckminster Fuller, so they named the new structure buckminster fullerene. There are 60 carbon atoms in buckminster fullerene. It is written as C_{60}.

FIGURE 4: One of the architect Buckminster Fuller's geodesic domes.

There are plans to use nanotubes in catalysts, as semiconductors and even to make carbon fibres for tennis rackets. The fullerenes have the potential to be very useful in the future.

Nano versus bulk properties

Fullerenes are important because of the shapes of the individual particles – balls or tubes, sieves or cages. They are minuscule structures – nanostructures first and chemicals second. **Nano properties** are different from **bulk properties**. Bulk chemical properties are the normal properties of large amounts of a material. Fullerenes do have bulk chemical properties – they dissolve in petrol – but that is not why they are important.

QUESTIONS

9 Suggest why nanotubes are better than bucky balls for making fibres.

10 There are plans to use bucky balls as lubricants. Suggest why they might be good for this.

Graphite

Graphite is made from flat layers that are far apart. Look back at the structure of graphite in Figure 2. The forces between the layers are weak (shown by green lines on the diagram), so the layers slide over each other very easily.

The atoms inside each layer are held together by covalent bonds. Each layer is a giant structure. This gives graphite a high melting point, like diamond.

There are free electrons on each layer. The electrons can move, they are **delocalised**, so they conduct electricity. Diamond does not have free electrons, so does not conduct electricity.

Fullerene uses

Ball-shaped fullerenes – bucky balls – can act as cages to trap other molecules. Their uses could be:

- to carry drug molecules around the body and deliver them to where they are needed
- to trap dangerous substances in the body and remove them.

Nanotubes can be used in catalyst systems. Atoms of catalyst can be attached to the nanotubes. The nanotube has a large surface area, so there is more chance of the reactants colliding with the catalyst.

Molecular manufacture

Nanoparticles are made in a different way from normal chemicals. Instead of finding a reaction that produces the chemical, one type of nanoparticle is used and then bits are knocked off or stuck on until it is the desired shape. Structural engineering is happening at a molecular level!

QUESTIONS

11 Fullerenes do not conduct electricity. Suggest **two** reasons why.

12 Scientists plan to attach atoms of precious-metal catalysts to nanotubes instead of using small lumps of solid metal as a catalyst. Suggest and explain **one** advantage of this method.

How pure is our water?

You will find out:
- what water is used for
- about some common pollutants in water
- how drinking water is purified

We think we know what water is used for, but do we?

We use water for lots of things – showering, washing the car and cooking at home, but nearly half of the water used in the UK cools power stations!

Water to cool power stations doesn't need putrifying.

Where do we get water from?

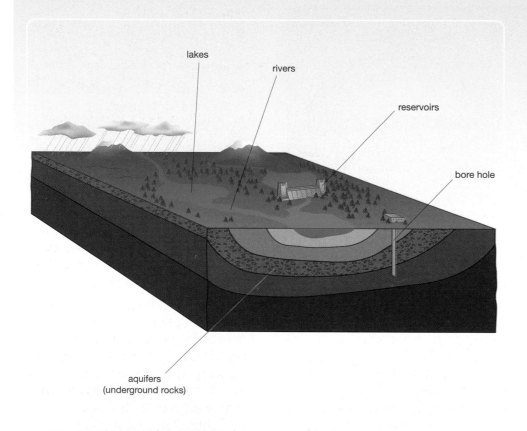

lakes

rivers

reservoirs

bore hole

aquifers (underground rocks)

FIGURE 1: Where we get our water.

Water as a resource

Water used by industry is:
- a cheap raw material
- used as a coolant
- a valuable solvent.

What is in water before it is purified?
- Dissolved salts and minerals
- Pollutants
- Insoluble materials
- Microbes (these are killed by chlorination)

Pollutants in drinking water

What **pollutants** may get into tap water?
- Nitrate residues
- Lead compounds
- Pesticide residues

:: QUESTIONS ::

1 Suggest what happens to cooling water after it has been used.
2 Suggest where aquifers get their water.
3 Name **three** pollutants that sometimes get into tap water.

...bore hole ...chlorination ...distillation ...filtration

Water purification

The water in a river is cloudy and often not fit to drink. To turn it into the clean water in taps it is passed through a **water purification** works.

There are three main stages in water purification:

- **sedimentation** of particles – bits drop to the bottom
- **filtration** of very fine particles – using sand
- **chlorination** – kills microbes.

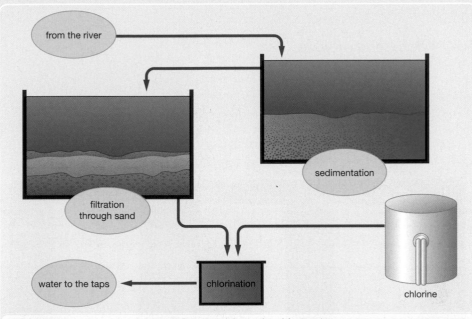

FIGURE 2: The steps in purification of water. Why is the chlorination step necessary?

In the figure: from the river; sedimentation; filtration through sand; chlorination; water to the taps; chlorine

How do pollutants get into drinking water?

Some pollutants get into the water before it has been purified and some get in after water has left the treatment works.

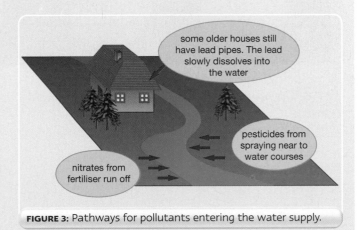

some older houses still have lead pipes. The lead slowly dissolves into the water

pesticides from spraying near to water courses

nitrates from fertiliser run off

FIGURE 3: Pathways for pollutants entering the water supply.

QUESTIONS

4 Which **two** pollutants come from agriculture?

5 Find out where your local water supply comes from. Will anyone have drunk the water already?

More on water purification

FIGURE 4: A sedimentation tank at a water treatment works.

Water from a **bore hole** is usually pure, so it needs little treatment. Water from a river needs much more doing to it.

- Sedimentation. Chemicals are added to make solid particles and bacteria settle out.
- Filtration. A layer of sand on gravel filters out the remaining fine particles. Some types of sand filter also remove microbes.
- Chlorination. Chlorine is added to kill microbes.

Some soluble substances remain in the water. Some of these can be poisonous, for example pesticides and nitrates. These are treated by extra processes.

Seawater has so many substances dissolved in it that it is undrinkable. Techniques such as **distillation** must be used to remove the dissolved substances. Distillation takes huge amounts of energy, so it is very expensive. It is only used when there is not enough fresh water.

QUESTIONS

6 Which stage in distillation makes the process so expensive?

7 Suggest why the chlorination stage of water purification comes last.

Precipitation reactions for testing water

One test to see what is in water is a **precipitation reaction**.

You will find out:
- how to test for sulfates, chlorides, bromides and iodides
- about precipitation reactions
- about the importance of conserving water

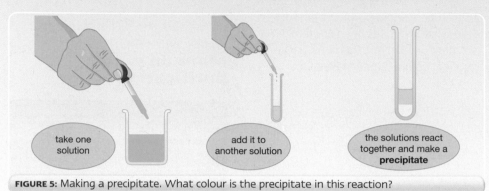

take one solution

add it to another solution

the solutions react together and make a **precipitate**

FIGURE 5: Making a precipitate. What colour is the precipitate in this reaction?

It is easy to test for some of the **ions** that might be dissolved in water using precipitation reactions.

Test for sulfate ions

Add one or two drops of barium chloride solution to the water in the test tube.

Sulfates give a white precipitate.

Test for chloride, bromide and iodide ions

Add one or two drops of silver nitrate solution to the water in the test tube.

Chlorides give a white precipitate.

Bromides give a cream precipitate.

Iodides give a yellow precipitate.

FIGURE 6: Using precipitation reactions to find what ions are present in water.

QUESTIONS

8   What solution is used to test for chlorides?

9   What colour precipitate do chlorides produce?

...ion   ...precipitate

Water tests

In a precipitation reaction, two solutions react to form a chemical that does not dissolve. This chemical suddenly appears in the liquid as a solid, a precipitate.

| lead nitrate | + | sodium sulfate | $\longrightarrow$ | lead sulfate (white precipitate) | + | sodium nitrate |

| silver nitrate | + | sodium chloride | $\longrightarrow$ | silver chloride (white precipitate) | + | sodium nitrate |

| silver nitrate | + | sodium bromide | $\longrightarrow$ | silver bromide (cream precipitate) | + | sodium nitrate |

| silver nitrate | + | sodium iodide | $\longrightarrow$ | silver iodide (yellow precipitate) | + | sodium nitrate |

Clean water

Clean water saves more lives than medicines. That is why, after disasters and in developing countries, relief organisations concentrate on providing clean water supplies. In Europe, in 1892, river-borne cholera killed 8500 people in Hamburg, which took its drinking water from the river Elbe. Downstream in Altona they drank the same water plus Hamburg's sewage. But Altona put its water through simple sand filters, and almost no one died.

Water conservation

Water is a **renewable** resource. However, that does not mean that the supply is endless. If there is not enough rain in the winter, reservoirs do not fill up properly for the rest of the year. In the UK today more and more homes are being built, which increases the demand for water.

Producing tap water does have costs. It takes energy to pump and to purify it – all of which increases global warming.

QUESTIONS

10 If there is a major power cut it is possible for water taps to stop working. Suggest why.

11 What would you see if you added silver nitrate solution to potassium iodide solution?

12 What would you see if you added silver nitrate solution to calcium chloride solution?

13 Tap water samples give a positive test for chloride ions.
Suggest why.

Water tests

The balanced symbol equations for the precipitation reactions are:

$$Pb(NO_3)_{2(aq)} + Na_2SO_{4(aq)} \longrightarrow PbSO_{4(s)} + 2NaNO_{3(aq)}$$

$$AgNO_{3(aq)} + NaCl_{(aq)} \longrightarrow AgCl_{(s)} + NaNO_{3(aq)}$$

$$AgNO_{3(aq)} + NaBr_{(aq)} \longrightarrow AgBr_{(s)} + NaNO_{3(aq)}$$

$$AgNO_{3(aq)} + NaI_{(aq)} \longrightarrow AgI_{(s)} + NaNO_{3(aq)}$$

EXAM HINTS AND TIPS

Remember that Pb^{2+} ions and SO_4^{2-} ions are doubly charged.

QUESTIONS

14 Write a balanced symbol equation for the reaction between silver nitrate solution and potassium iodide solution.

15 Write a balanced symbol equation for the reaction between silver nitrate solution and calcium chloride, $CaCl_2$.

...precipitation reaction   ...renewable

Module summary

Concept map

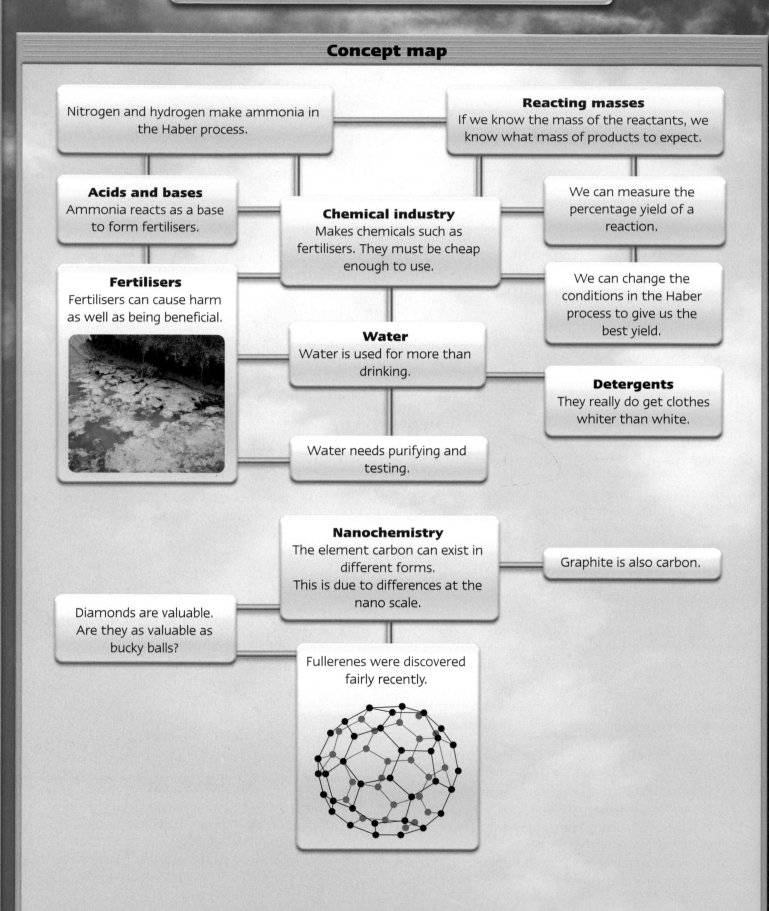

Nitrogen and hydrogen make ammonia in the Haber process.

Reacting masses
If we know the mass of the reactants, we know what mass of products to expect.

Acids and bases
Ammonia reacts as a base to form fertilisers.

Chemical industry
Makes chemicals such as fertilisers. They must be cheap enough to use.

We can measure the percentage yield of a reaction.

We can change the conditions in the Haber process to give us the best yield.

Fertilisers
Fertilisers can cause harm as well as being beneficial.

Water
Water is used for more than drinking.

Detergents
They really do get clothes whiter than white.

Water needs purifying and testing.

Nanochemistry
The element carbon can exist in different forms.
This is due to differences at the nano scale.

Graphite is also carbon.

Diamonds are valuable. Are they as valuable as bucky balls?

Fullerenes were discovered fairly recently.

Module quiz

1 Copy and complete the word equation: acid + base → _____ + _____

2 Give **three** uses of sulfuric acid.

3 What is the relative formula mass of CH_4? (Relative atomic masses: H = 1, C = 12)

4 If a reaction yield is 100%, what does this tell you?

5 State **three** essential elements for plant growth.

6 What do we call the polluting effect of fertilisers in water?

7 Which acid reacts with which base to make ammonium sulfate?

8 What is the formula of ammonia?

9 What catalyst is used in the Haber process?

10 What does the symbol ⇌ tell you?

11 What is 'dry' in the process of dry cleaning?

12 State **four** factors that affect the cost of making and developing a new medicine.

13 Outline **three** main stages in extracting a chemical from plants.

14 Which of these are made by a batch process?
   ammonia   medicines   sulfuric acid

15 What are the **three** forms of carbon?

16 Why does diamond have such a high melting point?

17 Give **two** properties of graphite that make it useful as an electrolyte for molten substances.

18 Suggest **one** use for nanotubes.

19 Outline the **three** main stages in the purification of drinking water.

20 How would you test for chloride ions? Name the reagent and what you would see.

Numeracy activity

The total water abstraction in the UK is about 17 billion cubic metres.

QUESTIONS
1 Draw a pie chart to show the use of water in the UK.
2 What is the largest use of water?
3 What is the second largest use of water?
4 What is the third largest use of water?

		Amount in billion cubic metres
purified	domestic use	3.4
	services	1.5
	manufacturing	2.4
not purified	agriculture & fisheries	2.4
	energy	7.2

Exam practice

Exam practice questions

1 a Copy and complete the following sentences using the words below.

| more | water | less |
| alkali | salt | hydroxide |
| carbonate |

Universal indicator can be used to show the pH of a solution. Acids have a pH of _____ than 7. When an acid reacts with a metal oxide or a metal _____ the acid is neutralised and a _____ is formed. Acids also react with _____ to make a salt, carbon dioxide and _____ . If a metal hydroxide dissolves in water an _____ forms and this has a pH of _____ than 7. [7]

b Write a word equation for the reaction between sulfuric acid and copper oxide. [2]

c Write a balanced symbol equation for the reaction of sodium hydroxide and hydrochloric acid. [3]

[Total 12 marks]

2 a Ammonia is made in industry by reacting nitrogen and hydrogen. The reaction is reversible. The conditions used are high pressure, a temperature of 450 °C and a catalyst.
  i Write a word equation for this reaction. [3]
  ii What is the purpose of the catalyst? [1]
  iii What happens to the unreacted nitrogen and hydrogen? [1]
  iv Is ammonia produced in a continuous or batch process? [1]
  v Give two uses for the ammonia formed. [2]

b Write a balanced symbol equation for the reaction. [2]

c i Does a high pressure give a high rate of reaction? [1]
  ii Does a high pressure give a good yield of ammonia? [1]

  iii Does a high temperature give a high rate of reaction? [1]
  iv Does a high temperature give a good yield of ammonia? [1]

[Total 14 marks]

3 a Pharmaceutical companies are sometimes criticised for charging a lot of money for drugs. Compared with the industrial production of ammonia the small-scale production of drugs, often by batch processes, is much more expensive. State three other reasons why pharmaceuticals cost so much to produce. [3]

b Pharmaceuticals may be made from raw materials that are synthetic or extracted from plants. What are the three steps by which a chemical can be extracted from plant material? [3]

[Total 6 marks]

4 a The following table shows the five components of a washing powder. Copy and complete the table to show what the ingredients are.

Ingredient	What it does
	cleans
	softens hard water
	removes stains
	gives a 'whiter than white' appearance
	removes food stains in low temperature washes

[5]

b What is the advantage of using a low-temperature wash? [1]

c Washing-up liquid contains a detergent that is often a salt. What two types of substance are added to make a detergent? [2]

d Describe how a detergent works. [3]

[Total 11 marks]

Ammonia can be manufactured from nitrogen and hydrogen according to this equation.

$$N_2 + 3H_2 \longrightarrow 2NH_3$$

a The relative formula mass of N_2 is 28, H_2 is 2 and NH_3 is 17. If 14 kg of nitrogen are reacted with an excess of hydrogen in a small-scale process, what is the predicted yield of ammonia that could be formed? [2]

b In an industrial-scale process only 12 tonnes of ammonia were made when the predicted possible yield of 48 tonnes was possible. Calculate the percentage yield this represents. [2]

c i A student wants to make some ammonium nitrate fertiliser in the laboratory and uses the equipment opposite. Add labels to each diagram to say what each piece of apparatus is called. [3]

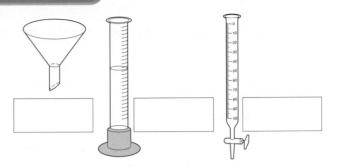

ii State which acid and which alkali the student will need to make the fertiliser. [2]

d i The use of fertilisers can lead to water pollution. Describe how this can occur. [2]

ii As well as soluble pollutants, water to be used for supplying the public must be treated to remove other pollutants before use. Give two other substances that may be present in such water and explain how each may be removed. [4]

---

a

N_2	+	$3H_2$	$\rightleftharpoons$	$2NH_3$
$2 \times 14 = 28$				$2(14 + 3) = 34$
so 28 kg			$\longrightarrow$	34 kg
and 14 kg			$\longrightarrow$	17 kg

Very clearly set out – a good answer.

Excellent. The student has stated the equation to be used and worked methodically through the calculation.

b % yield = $\dfrac{actual\ yield}{predicted\ yield} \times 100\% = \dfrac{12}{48} \times 100\% = 25\%$

c i

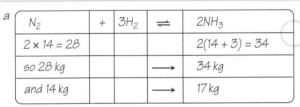

filter funnel

measuring jug

burette

c i The middle label should read measuring cylinder (not 'jug'). Often it is the simple questions that lose a student marks.

ii ammonia (the alkali) and nitric acid.
d i The fertiliser gets into the water supply.
ii Microbes must be removed and this can be done by treatment with chlorine. Insoluble material might be present and this can be filtered out.

ii This is correct.

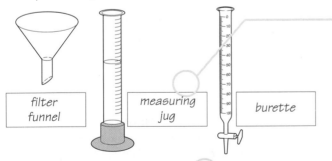

The student has not answered **d i**. They should have described how this happens. A good answer would have been: 'When rain falls it leaches the nitrates from the soil and the run-off enters streams or aquifers from which water is extracted'. Good answer to **d ii**.

Overall Grade: B

How to get an A

Be careful with questions like **d i**. You must take care not to simply repeat what is already written in the question. After you answer each question, check to see you haven't just repeated it – add more information if it is needed. Students often finish the exam early and close the paper. Don't do this! Check your answers and use this time to make sure you have exactly answered each question.

P3 Forces for transport

The bridge is exposed to winds of up to 150 km/h so side screens are used to reduce the effect of the wind by 50 per cent.

The Millau bridge is the world's highest road bridge. The roadway is 270 metres above the River Tarn, which is higher than the Eiffel Tower!

The Millau bridge, in southern France, connects the motorway networks of France and Spain. A Franco-British venture it was designed by Norman Foster to have 'the delicacy of a butterfly'. It is just one of many projects designed to improve transport and road safety for us all.

The masts rise 90 metres above the road.

The road is curved because a straight road could induce a sensation of floating for drivers.

CONTENTS

Speed

You will find out:
- how to calculate speed
- how to measure speed
- how speed cameras work

Caught on camera

A speeding motorist is caught on camera driving on a dual carriageway. The speed limit is 70 mph.

The speed camera was invented by a company founded by a rally driver!

Speed is a measure of how fast an object is going. To find the speed of an object the following need to be measured:

- how far an object moves
- the time the object takes to move.

The units of speed are m/s or km/h.

If a car travels at 80 km/h it covers a **distance** of 80 km in a **time** of 1 hour.

Measuring speed

In everyday situations a tape measure or trundle wheel and stopwatch are used to measure speed. In the laboratory a light gate and sensitive timer or data logger are used.

Using a speed camera

On roads, speed is often measured with a **speed camera**.

- As a speeding car passes a camera a photograph is taken.
- A second photograph is taken 0.5 seconds later. There are white lines painted on the road at distances of 1.5 m. They show how far the car travels in 0.5 seconds.
- For example, a car passes over six lines. It travels 1.5 × 6 = 9 m in 0.5 seconds.
- This means the speed of the car was 18 m/s or 65 km/h (about 40 miles per hour).

▯▯ QUESTIONS ▯▯

1. Sam ran 100 m in 18 seconds. Priya ran 120 m in the same time. Who ran the fastest?
2. Chris and Nisha see how far they can each cycle in 1 minute. Chris cycles a distance of 300 m and Nisha a distance of 380 m. Who cycles faster?

...average speed   ...distance   ...instantaneous speed

How fast?

$$\text{average speed} = \frac{\text{distance travelled}}{\text{time taken}} = \frac{d}{t} \quad \text{units are m/s or km/h}$$

example

A Formula 1 racing car driver completes a 560 km race in 2 hours.

$$\textbf{average speed} = \frac{d}{t} = \frac{560}{2} = 280 \text{ km/h}$$

'Average' speed is used because the speed of a car changes during a journey.

The speed at a certain point in time is called **instantaneous speed**.

example

A snail moves 5 mm in 10 seconds.

$$\text{average speed} = \frac{5}{10} = 0.5 \text{ mm/s} = 0.0005 \text{ m/s}$$

example

An aircraft travels 1800 km in 2 hours.

$$\text{average speed} = \frac{1800}{2} = 900 \text{ km/h} \qquad = \frac{900 \times 1000}{3600} = 250 \text{ m/s}$$

(Remember! 1 km = 1000 m, 1 hour = 60 x 60 = 3600 seconds.)

Speed limits

Different roads have different speed limits. The speed limit can depend on:

- the type of road such as single or dual carriageway, motorway, straight or winding
- the area the road is in such as town or country.

FIGURE 1: Roadside sign to show the speed limit. Suggest why it is dangerous for drivers to exceed speed limits.

QUESTIONS

3 Why is it impossible to maintain a constant speed during a car journey?

4 Ben drives from Norwich to Southampton, a distance of 320 km, in 4 hours. What is his average speed for the journey?

5 The speed limit on motorways is 70 mph (112 km/h). Reena drives 150 km in one and a half hours.
Does she break the speed limit?

6 Suggest **one** reason why the speed limit is higher on motorways than on other types of roads.

Rearranging the equation

If the average speed of a car is known it is possible to work out:

- distance travelled in a certain time

$$\text{distance travelled} = \text{average speed} \times \text{time}$$

- how long it takes to travel a known distance

$$\text{time taken} = \frac{\text{distance travelled}}{\text{average speed}}$$

Measuring average speed

To measure average speed, the distance travelled in a certain time must be known. The accuracy of the answer depends on the methods used to measure distance and time. Instruments such as car speedometers exist to give the speed of a car directly. A police officer uses a **radar gun** to measure the speed of a car.

FIGURE 2: A police officer using a radar gun to measure the speed of passing cars.

QUESTIONS

7 Estimate how far a snail would travel in 1 hour.

8 Tom averages 48 km/h on his 12 km journey to school. How long does his journey take?

Looking at motion

Looking at moving cars is important for road planners, road safety experts and car manufacturers.

Drawing a graph of distance against time shows how the distance moved by a car from its starting point changes over time.

You will find out:

- how to interpret simple graphs of distance against time
- how to draw distance–time graphs
- how to calculate speed from the gradient of a distance–time graph

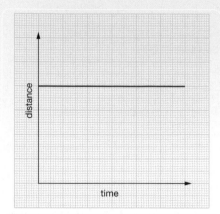

FIGURE 3: Graph of distance against time. The distance does not change over time so the car is stationary. What is its speed?

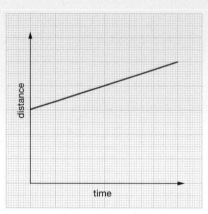

FIGURE 4: Graph of distance against time. The distance travelled by the car increases at a steady rate. It is travelling at a constant speed.

DID YOU KNOW?

Motorways account for about one-third of all road mileage but less than a tenth of road accidents.

QUESTIONS

9 Sketch a distance–time graph to show a car that travels a distance of 200 km in 2 hours at a constant speed, stops for half an hour and then travels a further 80 km in 1 hour. Remember to add a scale to the axes.

10 Sketch a possible distance–time graph for **one** of the cars travelling on the motorway system shown in the photograph on this page.

11 Kate plotted a distance–time graph for a bus as it approached her school.

Describe the motion of the bus. Give as much detail as you can.

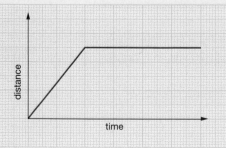

...best-fit straight line   ...curved line

Distance–time graphs

A distance–time graph shows how the distance moved by an object changes with time.

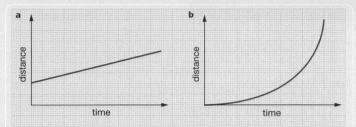

FIGURE 5: a The distance travelled by the object each second is the same. The gradient is constant so the speed is constant. **b** The distance travelled by the object each second increases as the time increases. The gradient increases so there is an increase in the speed of the object.

example

Distance–time graphs allow a collection of data to be shown. It is easier to interpret data when they are plotted on a graph than when they are listed in a results table.

Distance in m	Time in seconds
0	0
1	12
2	25
3	40
4	51
5	66
6	80

Gracie records the movement of a duck over time. She plots her results in a graph.

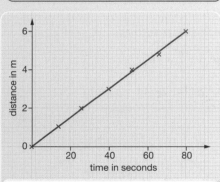

FIGURE 6: Graph showing the duck's movement over time. Gracie draws a **best-fit straight line** through the points on her graph.

QUESTIONS

12 Suggest why the points on Gracie's graph were not all exactly on a straight line.

13 Sketch a distance–time graph for a car that is slowing down.

14 A car travels a distance of 120 km in 1·5 hours at a constant speed. Sketch a distance–time graph for the car.

More on distance–time graphs

Speed is equal to the **gradient** (steepness) of a distance-time graph.

example

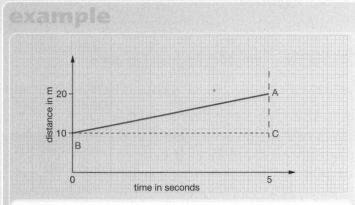

FIGURE 7: Graph of distance travelled by an object over time.

The gradient of the graph is:

$$\text{gradient} = \frac{AC}{BC} = \frac{(20-10)}{(5-0)} = \frac{10}{5} = 2 \qquad \text{speed} = 2 \text{ m/s}$$

- The larger the gradient (the steeper the line) the higher the speed.
- A **straight line** indicates the speed is constant. A **curved line** shows that the speed is changing.
- If the gradient increases the speed increases.
- If the gradient decreases the speed decreases.

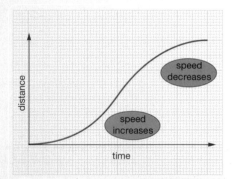

FIGURE 8: Graph of distance against time. What is the relationship between gradient and speed?

QUESTIONS

15 Look at the distance–time graph. Describe in words how the speed changes over time.

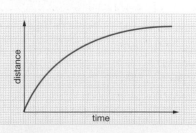

16 A cheetah chases a small animal at a constant speed and covers 200 m in 10 seconds before stopping suddenly. Sketch a distance–time graph and use it to find the speed of the cheetah.

Changing speed

You will find out:

- how to analyse speed–time graphs
- how to calculate acceleration from a speed–time graph
- how to find the distance travelled from a speed–time graph

Quick, quick, slow

Formula 1 racing cars race round bends on Grand Prix race tracks.

To do this they slow down – just a little – as they go into a bend and speed up very rapidly as they turn out of it.

All cars need to speed up and slow down frequently during a journey but not as rapidly as Formula 1 racing cars!

Speed–time graphs

A speed–time graph shows how the **speed** of an object changes with **time**.

The **gradient** (slope) of a line tells us how the speed is changing.

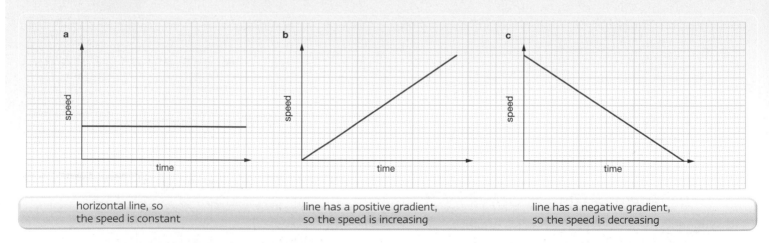

horizontal line, so the speed is constant

line has a positive gradient, so the speed is increasing

line has a negative gradient, so the speed is decreasing

QUESTIONS

1. A car brakes. Does the speed–time graph for the car show a positive or a negative gradient?
2. Sketch a speed–time graph for a tube train travelling between two stations.

EXAM HINTS AND TIPS

Don't confuse distance–time and speed–time graphs. Always look at the axes carefully.

...acceleration ...area ...deceleration ...distance

Speed-time graphs

Acceleration

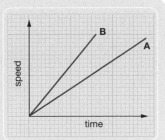

The lines **A**, **B**, **C** and **D** on the graphs show how the speeds of four cars change over time.

- The speeds of cars **A** and **B** are increasing.
- Line **B** is steeper than line **A**. It has a larger positive gradient.
- The speed of car **B** is increasing more rapidly than that of car **A**.
- Car **B** has a larger **acceleration** than car **A**.
- The speeds of cars **C** and **D** are decreasing.
- Line **D** is steeper than line **C**. It has a larger negative gradient.
- The speed of car **D** is decreasing more rapidly than that of car **C**.
- Car **D** has a larger negative acceleration (**deceleration**) than car **C**.

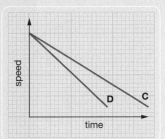

Distance travelled

Look again at the graphs above.

- The speed of car **B** is increasing more rapidly than the speed of car **A**, so car **B** is travelling further than car **A** in the same time.
- The **area** under line **B** is greater than the area under line **A**, for the same time.
- The speed of car **D** is decreasing more rapidly than the speed of car **C**, so car **D** is not travelling as far as car **C** in the same time.
- The area under line **D** is smaller than the area under line **C**, for the same time.

> The area under a speed-time graph is equal to the **distance** travelled.

QUESTIONS

3 The photograph shows two 100 m runners at the start of a race.

   a Which sprinter, **A** or **B**, has the greater acceleration out of the starting blocks?

   b On the same axes, sketch possible speed–time graphs for sprinter **A** and sprinter **B**.

   c What is the same for both sprinters?

Interpreting speed-time graphs

Calculating acceleration

The gradient (slope) of a speed-time graph is the acceleration.

example

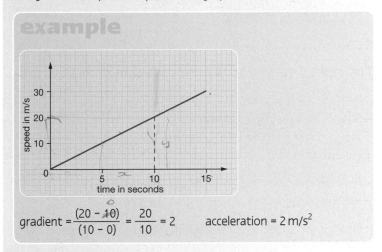

$$\text{gradient} = \frac{(20 - 10)}{(10 - 0)} = \frac{20}{10} = 2 \qquad \text{acceleration} = 2\,\text{m/s}^2$$

Calculating distance travelled

Look again at the graph above.

Distance travelled = area under speed-time graph

$$= \frac{1}{2} \times 10 \times 20 = 100\,\text{m}$$

The speed of a car does not usually remain constant for long or vary in the linear way shown above.

The graph below shows a car moving between two sets of traffic lights. The speed of the car is not changing uniformly so the acceleration is not constant. The area under the graph is **estimated** to find the distance travelled.

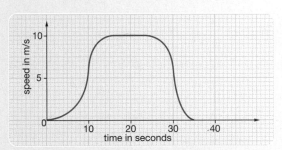

QUESTIONS

4 Describe in as much detail as possible the motion of a train that has the graph shown here. How far did the train travel?

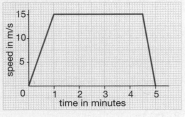

Acceleration

The table shows how the speed of a car changes as it starts to move.

Time in seconds	Speed in m/s
0	0
1	5
2	10
3	15
4	20
5	25

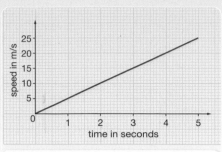

FIGURE 2: Graph of speed against time. What does the graph show?

You will find out:

- about acceleration
- about the relationship between acceleration, speed and time
- more about how to find the acceleration from a speed–time graph

The speed of the car increases by a constant amount every second. It increases by 5 m/s.

A change of speed is called acceleration. Acceleration is measured in m/s^2 (metres per second squared). The car has a constant acceleration of 5 m/s^2.

This table shows how the speed of a car changes as it comes to a stop.

Time in seconds	Speed in m/s
0	25
1	20
2	15
3	10
4	5
5	0

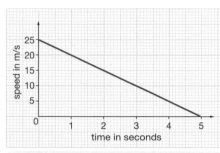

FIGURE 3: Graph of speed against time. What does the graph show?

The speed of the car decreases by a constant amount every second. It decreases by –5 m/s.

The car has a constant deceleration of 5 m/s^2. Its acceleration is –5 m/s^2.

FIGURE 1: A rocket needs a huge acceleration at lift-off.

 An object at a constant acceleration is different to an object at a constant speed.

▥ QUESTIONS ▥

5   Car **A** accelerates from 0 to 20 m/s in 15 seconds. Car **B** accelerates from 0 to 30 m/s in 12 seconds. Which car, **A** or **B**, has the greater acceleration?

6   A train accelerates from 0 to 20 m/s in 100 seconds and then decelerates, stopping 250 seconds after it started. Which is greater, its acceleration or deceleration?

...direction   ...tangentially

Acceleration

During a car journey the speed of the car increases and decreases. It does not stay constant.

A change in speed per unit time is called acceleration.

$$\text{acceleration} = \frac{\text{change in speed}}{\text{time taken}}$$

units are m/s^2 or km/h^2

An advertisement for a new car often boasts a rapid acceleration.

A speed of 108 km/h is $\frac{108 \times 1000}{60 \times 60}$ = 30 m/s

$$\text{acceleration} = \frac{\text{change in speed}}{\text{time taken}} = \frac{(30 - 0)}{6} = 5 \, m/s^2$$

This means the speed of the car increases by 5 m/s every second.

Suppose the car slows down to a stop in 15 seconds.

$$\text{acceleration} = \frac{\text{change in speed}}{\text{time taken}} = \frac{(0 - 30)}{15} = -2 \, m/s^2$$

The negative acceleration shows the car is slowing down, or decelerating. What gradient would the speed–time graph show?

▦ QUESTIONS ▦

7 The speed of a car increases from 10 m/s to 30 m/s in 8 seconds. Find its acceleration.

8 Luigi is travelling at 24 m/s. He brakes and comes to a stop in 30 seconds. Find his deceleration.

9 a Jane is driving at a speed of 72 km/h. Convert this to m/s.

   b She accelerates to 108 km/h in 8 seconds. Calculate her acceleration.

EXAM HINTS AND TIPS

Make sure you can change the subject of the acceleration equation. Practise until you find it easy.

$$\text{acceleration} = \frac{\text{change in speed}}{\text{time taken}}$$

$$\text{change in speed} = \text{acceleration} \times \text{time}$$

$$\text{time taken} = \frac{\text{change in speed}}{\text{acceleration}}$$

Accelerating at a constant speed

A vehicle may go round a roundabout at a constant speed but it is accelerating! This is because the **direction** of its movement is changing. It is not going in a straight line.

The driver needs to apply a force towards the centre of the roundabout to change direction to stop the vehicle from travelling in a straight line. This force gives the vehicle an acceleration directed towards the centre of the roundabout. The vehicle does not accelerate in the direction in which it is moving.

FIGURE 4: Vehicles travelling round a roundabout. Why may the speed of each vehicle be constant when it is accelerating?

This is true for any object that changes its direction of travel. It moves **tangentially** to a circle or arc of a circle.

Velocity is the speed of a moving object in a known direction.

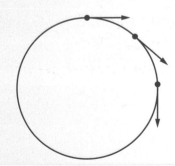

FIGURE 5: A moving object that changes its direction of travel moves tangentially to a circle or its arc.

▦ QUESTIONS ▦

10 Describe what happens if a car driver drives round a roundabout too fast.

11 A car has a maximum acceleration of $4 \, m/s^2$. How long does it take the car to reach a speed of 36 m/s, starting from rest?

Forces and motion

You will find out:

- about when a force acts on an object to speed it up or slow it down
- how mass, force and acceleration are linked
- how to use the equation $F = ma$
- about the forces between two objects

Be safe!

Most people are keen to learn to drive as soon as they reach the legal age to drive of 17.

The thrill of passing a driving test and gaining the freedom that it brings takes some beating.

A basic understanding of the forces acting on a moving vehicle can help to make drivers safe.

What do forces do?

To **accelerate** in a car the driver presses on the accelerator pedal. This increases the **pull** of the engine that provides a forward **force**. If they press the pedal down further, the pull of the engine is greater and the acceleration increases.

FIGURE 1: These cars have the same engines and so they have the same forward force. Car **a** has a smaller mass and a larger acceleration. Car **b** has a larger mass and a smaller acceleration.

For the same forward force:	For the same mass:	For the same acceleration:
more mass has less acceleration	more force causes more acceleration	a large mass needs a large forward force
less mass has more acceleration	less force causes less acceleration	a small mass needs a small forward force

■ QUESTIONS ■

1 **a** Meera is playing tennis. What happens to the motion of the tennis ball when she hits it harder?

   b She hits a football with the same force. How does the acceleration of the football compare with that of the tennis ball?

2 Ben is driving along a road and wants to go faster. He puts his foot on the accelerator. How does this change the force acting on his car?

...accelerate ...balanced ...force ...friction ...net

Force, mass and acceleration

If the forces acting on an object are **balanced** it is at rest or has a constant **speed**. If the forces acting on an object are unbalanced it speeds up or slows down. There is a **net** force acting.

FIGURE 2: In both these actions the forces are unbalanced, making the golf ball speed up and the Space shuttle slow down.

Three **variables** that affect the motion of an object are:

- unbalanced force, F
- mass, m
- acceleration, a.

Experimental work shows that:

- F is **proportional** to m if a is constant
- F is proportional to a if m is constant
- a is proportional to $\frac{1}{m}$ if F is constant.

Combining these, F is proportional to $m \times a$.

$F = ma$ the unit of force, F, is the **newton** (N) where m is in kg, a is in m/s^2

example

Donna pulls a sledge of mass 5 kg with an acceleration of 2 m/s^2 in the snow.

Watch Out When using $F = ma$, the units for m must be kg and for a must be m/s^2.

The force needed to do this is: $F = ma$
$F = 5 \times 2 = 10\,N$

Donna needs to pull harder than this because:

- there are **friction** forces acting backwards
- she pulls the sledge at an angle to the ground.

QUESTIONS

3 Explain why a parachute is used as the Space shuttle lands.

4 What net force is needed to give a car of mass 1000 kg an acceleration of 4 m/s^2?

More on $F = ma$

The equation $F = ma$ is used to find mass or acceleration if the resultant force is known.

example

Professional golfers such as Tiger Woods hit a golf ball with a force of approximately 9000 N. If the mass of the ball is 45 g, the acceleration during the very short time (about 0.005 milliseconds) of impact can be calculated.

$$a = \frac{F}{m} = \frac{9000}{0.045} = 200\,000\,m/s^2$$

Pairs of forces

Forces always occur in pairs.

When two vans collide the forces on each are of equal size but in opposite directions, $F_1 = F_2$.

From Figure 3:

$F_E = F_M$

The forces in the pair:

- are the same size
- are in opposite directions
- act on different objects.

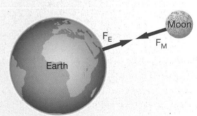

F_E = force on Earth due to Moon
F_M = force on Moon due to Earth

FIGURE 3: The Moon orbits Earth due to the gravitational force of attraction between it and Earth.

 Watch Out The pairs of forces are not balanced forces.

QUESTIONS

5 A car with a mass of 1200 kg has a resultant forward force acting on it of 4200 N. Find its acceleration.

6 The two vans shown above collide. Why is the driver of the big van safer?

Road safety

A car driver cannot stop a car immediately. It takes the driver time to react to danger. This is called **thinking time**. The higher the speed of a car the larger the distance it travels while a driver thinks.

Thinking distance is the distance travelled between a driver seeing a danger and taking action to avoid it, such as putting their foot on the brake pedal to stop the car.

Braking distance is the distance travelled before a car comes to a stop after the brakes have been applied. Braking distance increases as the speed of the car increases.

> **stopping distance** = thinking distance + braking distance

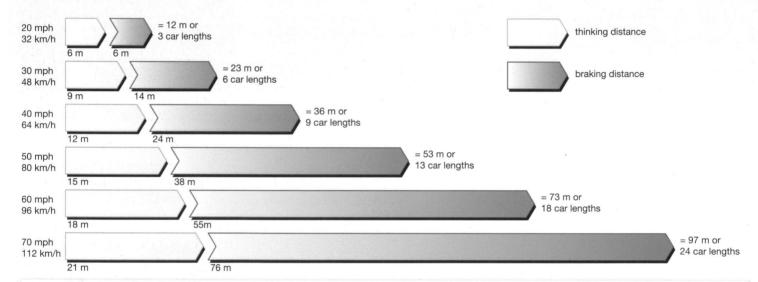

FIGURE 4: How speed affects stopping distance for an average family car, driven by an alert driver on a dry road. Why do you think the road conditions, for example wet or dry, affect stopping distance?

QUESTIONS

7   Why should a car be a greater distance behind the car in front on a motorway than on a road in a town?

8   Mohammed is driving along a busy road. The brake lights of the car in front come on but Mohammed does not brake immediately. Why not?

...brake pads   ...braking distance   ...friction   ...reaction time   ...stopping distance

Thinking distance

For an alert driver, thinking time (or **reaction time**) is about 0.7 seconds.

Thinking time and therefore thinking distance may increase if a driver is:

- tired
- under the influence of alcohol or other drugs
- distracted or lacks concentration.

An increase in thinking distance makes an accident more likely.

Braking distance

The braking distance may increase if:

- the road is icy or wet
- the car has poor brakes or bald tyres
- the car is travelling fast.

An increase in braking distance makes an accident more likely.

Driving safely

FIGURE 5: Traffic in heavy snow. Why must drivers slow down in these conditions?

The table of stopping distances on page 184 shows how important it is to:

- keep an appropriate distance from the car in front
- have different speed limits for different types of road
- slow down when road conditions are poor.

Factors affecting braking distance

- The greater the mass of a vehicle the greater its braking distance.
- The greater the speed of a vehicle the greater its braking distance.
- In a car braking system a disc rotates between two **brake pads**. When the brakes are applied the pads are pushed against the disc. This creates a large **friction** force that slows the car down.

FIGURE 6: A car disc brake.

- Worn **tyres** with very little **tread** reduce the grip of the wheels on a slippery road, leading to skidding and an increase in braking distance.

FIGURE 7: The treads on this tyre are worn. Why is this dangerous?

The Ministry of Transport (MOT) test for vehicles over 3 years old includes checks on brakes and tyres.

■■■■ QUESTIONS ■■■■

9 How does thinking distance increase as speed increases?

10 a How does braking distance increase as speed increases?

   b Suggest why road safety campaigns use slogans such as 'Kill your speed not a child!'

11 Estimate the stopping distance for a car travelling at 45 mph.

■■■■ QUESTIONS ■■■■

12 Formula 1 drivers use tyres with very little tread when the track surface is dry and tyres with more tread when the surface is wet. Suggest why.

...thinking distance   ...thinking time   ...tread   ...tyre

Work and power

You will find out:

- about everyday examples of doing work
- how to calculate work done
- that energy is needed to do work

Push and pull

Work is done whenever a force moves an object. Transport of all kinds involves motion. Different types of transport suit different environments. In big cities, buses or underground trains are convenient, while a cable car is an ideal way to get around in mountainous areas.

Work

Work is done when a **force** moves. People and machines do work.

When a person lifts a **mass** or pushes a shopping trolley work is done.

- The more massive the object lifted or the heavier the shopping in a trolley, the more work is done because a larger force is being moved.
- When the object or the trolley is moved a larger distance more work is done.

The amount of work done depends on the:

- size of the force acting on an object
- distance the object is moved.

When a person climbs stairs or jumps in the air the force moved is their **weight**.

Energy is needed to do work. Energy comes from food. The more work is done the more energy is needed.

A machine gets the energy it needs to do work from an energy source such as electricity, or energy resources such as gas or oil.

Work and energy are measured in **joules** (J).

FIGURE 1: This man is doing work. He is using a force to lift the box.

QUESTIONS

1 What unit is used to measure:
   a mass
   b work
   c energy?
2 Write down **two** things that affect the amount of work done by a force.

...energy   ...force   ...joule

More on work

Work is done when a force moves in the direction in which the force acts.

Weight is due to gravitational attraction and acts towards the centre of the Earth.

The amount of work done increases as:

■ the size of the force increases

■ the distance moved in the direction of the force increases.

FIGURE 2: **a** The jumping clown does work in raising his weight off the ground and **b** the woman is walking on a level pavement so no work is done to move her weight.

work done = force × distance moved (in the direction of the force)

units are joules (J)

example

If the clown above weighs 700 N, the work he does against gravity when he jumps 80 cm is:

work done = force × distance moved

    = 700 × 0.8 = 560 J

example

Santosh weighs 600 N. He is out walking and comes to a steep hill 1 km long marked with a slope of 20%. This is sometimes called a '1 in 5' hill. It means that for every kilometre travelled along the slope a vertical height of 0.2 km is climbed. The amount of work Santosh does in walking up the hill is:

work done = force × distance moved

    = 600 × 0.2 = 120 J

QUESTIONS

3   Would Santosh do more work if he ran, instead of walked, up the hill? Explain your answer.

4   How much work does Paul do when he lifts a box weighing 250 N off the floor to a shelf 2 m high?

Using the equation for work done

Rearranging the equation
work done = force × distance gives:

$$\text{force} = \frac{\text{work done}}{\text{distance}}$$

$$\text{distance} = \frac{\text{work done}}{\text{force}}$$

Car brakes

A car loses all its **kinetic energy** when it stops. The faster it is going the more kinetic energy it possesses. The kinetic energy is transferred mainly into heat by the brakes.

kinetic energy lost = work done by brakes

example

The brakes in a car produce a force of 5000 N and the car has to lose 200 000 J of kinetic energy.

work done by brakes = 200 000 J

work done = force × distance moved

The distance moved in stopping is equal to the braking distance, so:

$$\text{braking distance} = \frac{\text{work done by brakes}}{\text{braking force}}$$

$$= \frac{200\ 000}{5000}$$

$$= 40\,\text{m}$$

QUESTIONS

5   Tom does 3000 J of work in pushing a small van a distance of 10 m. How big is the friction force he has to push against?

6   Bethany is stacking a food shelf with tins each weighing 12 N. When she has put 20 tins on the shelf she calculates that she has done 288 J of work. How high is the shelf?

Power

Imagine a tall office block that has two lifts. One lift takes 40 seconds to go up to the tenth floor. The other newer lift takes 25 seconds.

Both lifts do the same amount of work but the new one does it more quickly. The new lift has a greater **power**.

Power is measured in **watts** (W).

A large amount of power is measured in **kilowatts** (kW). 1 kW = 1000 W.

Fuel consumption

Some cars are more powerful than others. They travel faster and cover the same distance in a shorter time. More powerful cars need to gain more energy every second and require more fuel.

FIGURE 3: Use the table below to help you decide which of these cars has the most power.

	Engine capacity in litres	Power in kW	Top speed in km/h	Fuel consumption in litres/100 km
green car	1.3	44	160	6
yellow car	3.6	240	285	11

QUESTIONS

7 Look at the table above. Which car, green or yellow, would go further on a litre of petrol?

8 On a building site, crane **A** lifts a steel girder on to a building in 60 seconds. Crane **B** takes 40 seconds to do the same job.

   a Does one crane do more work than the other?

   b Is one crane more powerful than the other?

...carbon dioxide ...greenhouse gas

Calculating power

$$power = \frac{work\ done}{time\ taken}$$

example

Anoushka runs up a flight of 16 stairs, each 0.2 m high, in 8 seconds.

She weighs 500 N.

She climbs a vertical height of:

16 × 0.2 = 3.2 m.

$$\frac{work}{done} = force \times \frac{distance\ moved\ in\ the}{direction\ of\ the\ force}$$

$$= 500 \times 3.2 = 1600\ J$$

$$power = \frac{work\ done}{time} = \frac{1600}{8} = 200\ W$$

If Anoushka walks up the stairs she takes 10 seconds.

$$Her\ power = \frac{1600}{10} = 160\ W$$

Car fuel consumption

■ Fuel is expensive and a car with a high fuel consumption is expensive to run, particularly over large distances.

■ The products of burning fuels pollute the environment. Car exhaust gases are harmful and the production and transport of fuels create many hazards.

Carbon dioxide emissions

The Government wants to reduce car emissions of **carbon dioxide** (CO_2). Carbon dioxide pollutes local air and is a major source of global **greenhouse gases**, which contribute to climate change. The amount of Vehicle Excise Duty paid is now based on carbon dioxide emissions. Vehicle manufacturers and purchasers are made more aware of the environmental impact of vehicles and the use of more fuel-efficient cars is encouraged.

QUESTIONS

9 Neil can lift 20 weights, each weighing 30 N, through a height of 2 m in 60 seconds.
Calculate Neil's power.

10 Sarah can do 24 step-ups in 30 seconds. The step is 12 cm high and Sarah weighs 560 N. Calculate Sarah's power.

11 Suggest how the production and transport of fuels harm the environment.

More on power

The power equation can be rearranged to find work done or time taken for a known power value.

$$work\ done = power \times time$$

$$time\ taken = \frac{work\ done}{power}$$

The Eurostar train provides a high-speed service through the Channel Tunnel from London to Paris and Brussels. As it travels through northern France it reaches a maximum speed of 186 mph (300 km/h) with its engine operating at a power of 2 MW (2 million watts).

When Eurostar travels at maximum speed the amount of work done, or energy transferred, in 2 hours is calculated by:

$$power = \frac{work\ done}{time}$$

work done = power × time

= 2 000 000 × (120 × 60)

= 14 400 000 000 J

At maximum power, 14.4 MJ of energy are transferred to other energy forms during a 2 hour journey.

The Eurostar takes about 2 hours and 30 minutes to complete the 400 km journey to Paris, averaging a speed of about 160 km/h. It operates at maximum power for only a short part of the journey.

QUESTIONS

12 A 25 kW motor raises a 5000 N load through a height of 40 m.
How long does it take?

Surf's up!

SELF-CHECK ACTIVITY

CONTEXT

Will is 15 and keen on surfing. It is too cold to do much in the winter but as soon as spring comes he and his friends get their boards out and head for the beach. This usually means a car ride and their parents take it in turns. Today it is Will's dad who is driving him and his friends to the beach. This means there will be four passengers in the car and four surfboards strapped to the roof, and this adds to the weight.

Will usually persuades his dad to put some decent music on in the car. He sneaks the volume up a bit as well. On the beach road the wind has been blowing the sand up and some is lying on the road.

Typical of beach roads, the road does not have any pavements and the ground on either side rises quite steeply, so there are pedestrians on the road as well as cars. A couple of lads are play-fighting and one ends up suddenly being pushed further out into the narrow road. Will's dad brakes hard and the car slows down and then slides. It comes to a rest about a metre away from the lad in the road, who gives a sheepish smile and jogs off. A couple of Will's mates swear. They all feel it was a bit of a close call.

STEP 1

Will's dad does a lot of driving – most of it is to and from his work, with just him in the car. He is reluctant to admit it but he was a bit surprised by how far the car travelled before it came to a halt. He was not travelling at any great speed because of the road being narrow and the presence of pedestrians. Why did it take longer for Will's dad to stop than he expected?

STEP 2

The stopping distance of the car is made up of thinking distance and braking distance. How might the thinking distance have been greater in this case?

190

One of the ways in which the greater braking distance can be explained is by using the concept of kinetic energy. How does this help?

The greater stopping distance can also be explained with reference to friction. How does friction affect stopping distance?

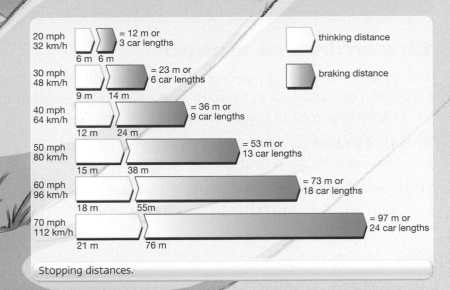

20 mph 32 km/h	= 12 m or 3 car lengths
6 m 6 m	
30 mph 48 km/h	= 23 m or 6 car lengths
9 m 14 m	
40 mph 64 km/h	= 36 m or 9 car lengths
12 m 24 m	
50 mph 80 km/h	= 53 m or 13 car lengths
15 m 38 m	
60 mph 96 km/h	= 73 m or 18 car lengths
18 m 55m	
70 mph 112 km/h	= 97 m or 24 car lengths
21 m 76 m	

□ thinking distance

▨ braking distance

Stopping distances.

Maximise your grade

These sentences show what you need to be including in your work. Use these to improve your work and to be successful.

Grade	Answer includes...
F	State **one** reason why it takes Will's dad longer to stop than expected.
	State **two** reasons why it takes Will's dad longer to stop than expected.
	Explain how distractions in the car affect thinking distance.
	Explain the role of friction in stopping a vehicle.
C	State the factors that affect kinetic energy.
	Explain the relationship between kinetic energy and braking distance.
A	Explain why the car initially starts to slow down, but then starts to slide.
	Research anti-lock braking systems and explain how the ABS system on Will's dad's car helped to avoid the accident.

Will's dad's car is fitted with ABS (anti-lock braking system).

a   Find out how ABS works.

b   What difference did ABS make to the braking distance in this case?

Energy on the move

You will find out:
- about kinetic energy
- how to calculate kinetic energy
- how to interpret data on fuel consumption
- how braking distance changes with speed

Dreaming of speed

Many people dream of owning a sleek powerful car like this Porsche with a top speed of 280 km/h (174 mph) and a fuel consumption of 11.4 litres/100 km (18 mpg) for its 3.6 litre engine.

Beautiful to look at and fun to drive it may be, but environmentally friendly it is not!

What do you think the cars of the future will look like? How do you think they will be powered?

Kinetic energy

Moving objects have **kinetic energy**.

There are different fuels that can be used to gain kinetic energy.

- The fuel for a cheetah is its food.
- The 'fuel' for a wind turbine is moving air.
- The aviation fuel for an aeroplane is obtained from **oil**.
- The fuel for a car is **petrol** or **diesel** oil.

FIGURE 1: The cheetah, the aeroplane and the blades on the wind turbine are all moving. What type of energy do moving objects have?

Petrol and diesel oil are **fossil fuels**. Some cars use more petrol or diesel oil than others and:

- cause more **pollution**, especially in cities
- cost more to run
- decrease supplies of **non-renewable** fossil fuels.

Scientists are experimenting with types of **renewable** fuels called **biofuels** such as organic wastes.

▥ QUESTIONS ▥

1. Which has the greatest kinetic energy, a cheetah or an aeroplane?
2. Give **two** ways in which a motorist could help to reduce their use of petrol or diesel.

...biofuel ...diesel ...fossil fuel ...kinetic energy ...mass

Braking distances

The table shows typical braking distances for cars at different speeds.

Speed		Braking distance in m
in m/s	in mph	
10	22	8
20	45	32
30	70	72
40	90	128

The braking distance increases with increasing speed, but not proportionally. When the speed doubles, the braking distance quadruples. The kinetic energy of the car also quadruples.

kinetic energy = $\frac{1}{2}mv^2$

where m = mass of an object in kg

v = speed of an object in m/s

the units are joules (J)

example

If a car has a mass of 1000 kg, its kinetic energy:
- at 20 m/s is $\frac{1}{2}mv^2 = \frac{1}{2} \times 1000 \times (20)^2 = 200\,000$ J
- at 40 m/s is $\frac{1}{2}mv^2 = \frac{1}{2} \times 1000 \times (40)^2 = 800\,000$ J.

When the car stops its kinetic energy changes into heat in the brakes, tyres and road.

work done by brakes = loss in kinetic energy

braking force × braking distance = change in kinetic energy

When the speed of the car doubles the kinetic energy and the braking distance quadruple.

This is why there are speed limits on roads and stiff penalties for drivers who exceed them.

What affects kinetic energy?

- A person has more kinetic energy at running pace than at walking pace.
- When a lorry and a car are travelling at the same speed a lorry has more kinetic energy.

Kinetic energy increases with:
- increasing **mass**
- increasing **speed**.

FIGURE 2: When travelling at the same speed, which vehicle – the car or the lorry – has greater kinetic energy?

Fuel consumption

Fuel consumption data are based on ideal road conditions and a car being driven at a steady speed. Values are obtained in urban and non-urban conditions.

Car	Fuel	Engine size in litres	Miles per gallon in mpg	
			urban	non-urban
Renault Megane	petrol	2.0	25	32
Land Rover	petrol	4.2	14	24

QUESTIONS

3. Why does an adult have more kinetic energy than a child when they are running at the same speed?

4. Look at the table of fuel consumption data above.
   a Suggest **one** reason for the difference between urban and non-urban fuel consumption values.
   b Write down **one** other trend that you notice in the data.

QUESTIONS

5. Emma is driving her car at 15 m/s when the car 25 m in front of her brakes suddenly.
   a If Emma's car has a mass of 1200 kg, what is its kinetic energy at 15 m/s?
   b Use the table above to show that the braking distance at this speed is 18 m.
   c Use your answers to **a** and **b** to find the braking force.
   d Do you think Emma hits the car in front? Explain your answer.

Fuel for cars

Most cars use petrol or diesel as fuel.

Petrol and diesel are made from oil. Petrol is more **refined** than diesel oil.

Petrol cars and diesel cars need different engines.

- Fuel in a petrol engine is ignited by a spark from a spark plug.
- Fuel in a diesel engine is ignited by hot compressed air in a cylinder.

The same amount of diesel oil contains more energy than petrol. A diesel engine is more **efficient** than a petrol engine.

Engine size in litres	Fuel consumption in mpg	
	petrol	diesel
1.6	44	60
2.0	40	51

Electric cars

Engineers and scientists are developing **electric cars** that are battery driven or **solar-powered**.

FIGURE 3: **a** Milk floats are battery-driven but do not go very fast and can only travel a short distance before the batteries need recharging. **b** Newer electric cars can travel faster but still need recharging frequently. Why are scientists trying to find fuels other than oil for vehicles?

DID YOU KNOW?

This Dutch car is powered by sunlight. It uses technology developed at the European Space Agency. It won a 3000 km race in a time of just over 30 hours.

QUESTIONS

6 Find the average speed of the Dutch solar-powered car.
7 Write down **two** things about fuel consumption that you notice in the table above.

...efficient   ...electric car   ...environment

Environmental pollution

Exhaust fumes from petrol- and diesel-fuelled cars cause serious pollution in towns and cities.

Battery-driven cars do not pollute the local **environment**, but their batteries need to be recharged.

FIGURE 4: A lead-acid battery used to power an electric car. Depending on the number of cells used the batteries give a range of about 50 to 120 miles.

Recharging uses electricity from a power station. Power stations pollute the local atmosphere and cause acid rain. It can be argued that battery-powered cars still cause pollution.

FIGURE 5: This hybrid electric car has solar panels on its roof that convert sunlight into additional power to supplement its battery. It is less environmentally friendly than a car powered only by solar energy, but it is more practical. Can you suggest why?

The hybrid electric car shown in Figure 5 is ideal for use in urban areas but needs to be improved further before it becomes a realistic form of transport for long journeys.

QUESTIONS

8 Give **two** problems associated with battery-powered cars.

9 a Give **two** advantages of solar-powered cars compared to battery-powered cars.

b What is the major problem associated with the use of solar-powered cars?

10 Comment on the statement above, 'It can be argued that battery-powered cars still cause pollution.'

Fuel consumption data

The fuel consumption data produced by car manufacturers and independent sources, such as specialist car magazines and the Consumers' Association, relate to ideal conditions. The distance covered by 1 L of fuel for a vehicle in practice is likely to be much less than the published value.

Factors that affect the fuel consumption of a car are:

- the amount of energy required to increase its kinetic energy
- the amount of energy required for it to do work against friction
- its speed
- the way in which it is driven such as excessive acceleration and deceleration, constant braking, speed changes
- road conditions, such as a rough surface.

Costs of alternative fuels

Alternative fuel sources are being developed for environmental reasons rather than cost. But electric cars are good value.

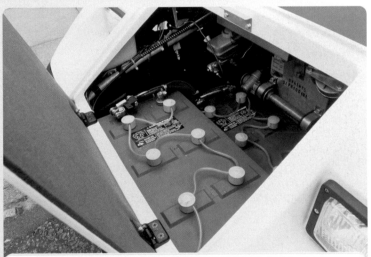

FIGURE 6: Batteries under the bonnet of the 'El-Jet' electric car are powered by a 7.5 kW motor and take 6 hours to charge.

An electric car called the 'El Jet' has a top speed of 70 km/h and a range of 70 km. It is claimed to have a running cost of about 5 p/km compared with 18 p/km for a petrol-driven car of a similar size.

QUESTIONS

11 Fuel consumption data are much better on a long journey using motorways than when driving on minor roads. Suggest why.

12 Suggest why fuel consumption data are unlikely to be achieved in normal driving conditions.

Crumple zones

You will find out:

- about the typical safety features that modern cars have
- how seatbelts, crumple zones and air bags act in a crash
- how forces can be reduced in a crash

Car safety

To stop a car safely energy must be absorbed.

Sometimes people say, 'They don't make cars like they used to,' when they see the damage caused to a modern car by a fairly minor accident. But modern cars are built with crumple zones at the front and rear so that the car absorbs the maximum amount of energy with the minimum injury to the driver and passengers.

Car safety

A moving car has **kinetic energy**. If a car is involved in a collision it has to lose kinetic energy very quickly. Modern cars have safety features that absorb **energy** when a vehicle stops suddenly such as:

- **brakes** that get hot
- **crumple zones** at front and rear that change shape
- **seatbelts** that stretch a little
- **air bags** that inflate and squash.

These safety features all absorb energy so that less has to be absorbed by the people in the car. This reduces or avoids injury.

A seatbelt and an air bag work together. On **impact**:

- the air bag inflates
- the seatbelt stretches and slows the forward motion of the driver's body.

In this way the head and thorax (chest) of the driver are protected.

FIGURE 1: An air bag and seatbelt in action during a car accident. What parts of the man are protected?

▪▪ QUESTIONS ▪▪

1. In addition to absorbing energy, in what other way does a seatbelt act to avoid serious injury?
2. Why are accidents at high speed more likely to cause serious injury than accidents at low speed?

...*acceleration* ...*air bag* ...*brakes* ...*crash barrier* ...*crumple zone* ...*energy*

More on car safety

On impact of a car:

- crumple zones absorb some of the car's energy by changing shape or 'crumpling'
- a seatbelt is designed to stretch a little so that some of the person's kinetic energy is converted to elastic energy

FIGURE 2: A simulated crash with a dummy with no seatbelt. How does wearing a seatbelt help to protect a person in a crash?

- an air bag absorbs some of the person's kinetic energy by squashing up around them.

FIGURE 3: Small children should travel in a child seat with a harness for maximum protection.

All these safety features:

- change shape
- absorb energy
- reduce injuries.

QUESTIONS

3 Why is a driver's air bag especially important?

4 Babies are often harnessed in a car seat that is strapped on the front passenger seat, facing the rear. Why must their air bag be switched off?

5 The young boy shown above is wearing a harness with wide straps. Suggest **one** reason why wide straps are used.

Reducing injury

To minimise injury, **forces** acting on the people in a car during an accident must be made as small as possible.

force = mass × acceleration

Force can be reduced by reducing the **acceleration**:

- by increasing stopping or collision time
- by increasing stopping or collision distance.

How do safety features work?

- Crumple zones increase the time between first impact and the car stopping.
- A seatbelt stretches a little and slows a person down more slowly.
- An air bag inflates on impact, slowing a person down more slowly and protecting them from protruding objects.
- A **crash barrier** is made from a material that changes shape readily on impact so the car travels further before stopping and takes longer to come to a halt.
- An **escape lane** on a steep hill allows a vehicle with failed brakes to stop more slowly by running into an upward slope with a rough surface.

FIGURE 4: An escape lane has a rough surface and an incline. Can you suggest why?

QUESTIONS

6 a Explain why you should always wear a seatbelt when travelling in the front seat of a car.

  b Explain why it is safer for the driver (as well as the front passenger) if the passenger behind is also wearing a seatbelt.

7 Crumple zones are included in the design of modern cars but they are only effective if the occupants all wear seatbelts. Explain why.

Safety features

Modern cars are built with many features designed to improve safety.

Active safety features

Active safety features directly improve the safety of a car and include:

- **ABS** brakes (**anti-lock** braking system)
- traction control (stops wheel spin)
- safety cage (protects in a roll-over accident).

Passive safety features

Passive safety features indirectly increase the safety of a car. They help a driver to concentrate on the road and reduce driver tiredness. They include:

- electric windows
- cruise control
- paddle shift controls (on the steering wheel)
- adjustable seating.

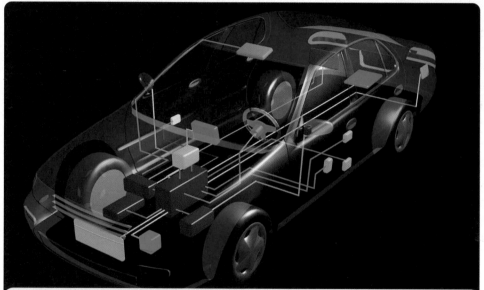

FIGURE 6: Computer-aided design (CAD) image of a modern car showing wiring and electronics for central locking, electric windows and powered mirror adjustment. Do these features directly or indirectly increase the safety of a car?

All safety features must be kept in good repair if they are to continue to be of benefit.

- Seatbelts must be replaced after a crash in case the belt fabric has been overstretched.
- The safety cage must be examined for possible damage after a crash.
- Seat fixings should be checked frequently to make sure they are secure.

You will find out:

- about some typical safety features of cars
- how safety features can make driving safer
- how ABS brakes reduce braking distances

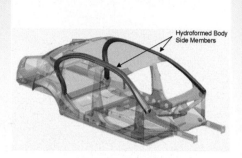

Hydroformed Body Side Members

FIGURE 5: A car safety cage. How does it make the car safer?

ABS brakes don't stop a car more quickly. They give improved control and prevent skidding.

QUESTIONS

8 How do electric windows contribute to road safety?

9 How does adjustable seating contribute to road safety?

...ABS ...active ...anti-lock

Making driving safer

Active safety features

- ABS brakes give a vehicle stability and maintain steering during hard braking in slippery conditions. Hard continuous pressure is needed to activate anti-lock brakes. The driver gets the maximum braking force without skidding and can still steer the car. The driver does not necessarily stop more quickly.

- Traction control stops the wheels on a vehicle from spinning when it accelerates rapidly. It gives maximum grip and stability on the road during acceleration.

FIGURE 7: What safety features help the driver keep control of the vehicle during this test?

- A car safety cage is a **rigid** frame that prevents the car from collapsing and crushing the occupants in a roll-over crash.

- Crumple zones at front and rear ends of the car keep damage away from the internal safety cage.

Passive safety features

- A cruise control system accelerates to a fixed speed irrespective of the load in the vehicle or the gradient of the road. It is less tiring on long motorway trips and avoids 'lead-foot syndrome', where the driver rests their foot too hard on the accelerator pedal and inadvertently speeds up.

- Electric windows open and close quickly at the push of a button leaving the driver to concentrate on driving.

- Paddle shift controls allow the driver to operate gears, lights, stereo and wipers without taking their hands off the steering wheel or their eyes off the road.

- Adjustable seating allows the driver's seat to be set in a safe, comfortable position.

QUESTIONS

10 Rate the active safety features mentioned above in order of importance in increasing car safety.

11 Rate the passive safety features mentioned above in order of importance in increasing car safety.

The ABS system

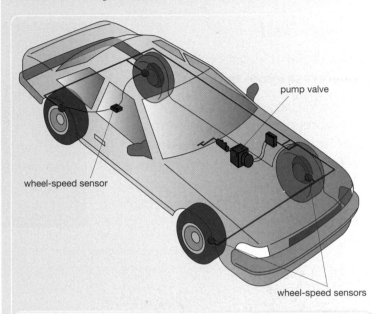

pump valve

wheel-speed sensor

wheel-speed sensors

FIGURE 8: The ABS braking system.

Wheel-speed sensors send information to a computer about the rotational speeds of the wheels. The computer controls the pressure to the brakes, via a pump, to prevent the wheels locking up. This increases the braking force (F) just before the wheels start to skid, stopping the car in a shorter distance (d).

> kinetic energy lost = work done by the brakes
>
> $$\tfrac{1}{2}mv^2 \qquad = \qquad F \times d$$
>
> where m = mass of car
>
> v = speed of car before braking

If F increases, d decreases and the braking distance decreases.

Saving lives

- Active safety features have a more immediate effect in saving lives in an accident.

- Passive safety features contribute to safe driving but do not directly affect the safety of a car driver and passengers in an accident.

QUESTIONS

12 Why are large cars safer than small cars?

13 ABS brakes stop a car of mass 1200 kg moving at 30 m/s in a distance of 75 m.
Find the braking force of the car.

Falling safely

You will find out:
- about the motion of falling objects
- how air resistance slows down falling objects
- about terminal speed

Free-fall

Free-fall parachutists fall for several kilometres before opening their parachutes.

They accelerate rapidly at first but soon reach a constant speed when the forces acting on them balance. When they open their parachutes they decelerate rapidly and gently float to the ground.

Falling objects

If an object is dropped it gets faster as it falls.

It is pulled towards the centre of Earth due to **gravity**.

There is a story that a famous scientist called Galileo dropped a small cannon ball and a large one from the leaning tower of Pisa in Italy to demonstrate the effect of gravity.

The balls hit the ground at the same time. This showed that all objects **accelerate** at the same rate (about 10 m/s^2), regardless of their mass.

But if a ball and a feather are dropped, the ball hits the ground first.

Objects that have a large area of **cross-section** such as parachutes, shuttlecocks or feathers, fall more slowly. This slowing down **force** is called **air resistance** or **drag**.

On the Moon and in outer Space there is no atmosphere and here objects with a large area of cross-section would also fall with an acceleration of 10 m/s^2.

FIGURE 1: Why does a shuttlecock fall slower than a ball?

DID YOU KNOW?

Apollo 15 landed safely after its mission to the Moon even though one of its parachutes failed.

QUESTIONS

1 If you drop a ball it accelerates. What happens if you throw it up?
2 Suggest why a parachutist falls more slowly after their parachute opens.

...*accelerate* ...*air resistance* ...*balanced* ...*cross-section* ...*drag*

Terminal speed

FIGURE 3: What happens to the speed of a parachutist when their parachute opens?

Parachutists

The speed of a **free-fall** parachutist changes as they fall to Earth. This is because the upward air resistance force on them changes.

Terminal speed is the maximum speed reached by a falling object. It occurs when forces acting on an object are **balanced**.

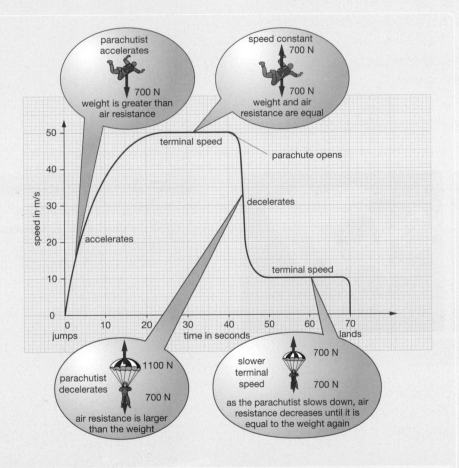

FIGURE 2: Graph to show the speed of a free-fall parachutist falling to Earth. What happens to the forces acting on the parachutist when the terminal speeds are reached?

- As the speed of a free-fall parachutist increases they displace more air **molecules** every second so the air resistance force increases. This reduces their acceleration.

- When their weight is equal to the air resistance force, the forces on them are balanced so they travel at a constant speed – the terminal speed.

- When the parachute opens the upward force on them increases suddenly as there is a much larger surface area, displacing more air molecules every second.

- They decelerate, displacing fewer air molecules each second, so the air resistance force decreases.

- Eventually they reach a new slower terminal speed when their weight is equal to the air resistance once more.

- This means they can land safely.

Drag racers and the Space shuttle also use parachutes to slow them down rapidly.

QUESTIONS

3 What would happen to the speed of a parachutist if their parachute failed to open?

4 Why do free-fall parachutists fall with their body in a horizontal position?

QUESTIONS

5 Ali and Charlie are free-fall parachutists. Ali weighs 500 N and Charlie weighs 800 N.
   Use your ideas about forces to explain who reaches the greatest terminal speed.

...force ...free-fall ...gravity ...molecule ...terminal speed

Frictional forces

forward force

drag

friction

FIGURE 4: Friction forces on a car. What do friction forces do?

You will find out:

- how friction forces affect motion
- how the shapes of moving objects influence their top speed
- about acceleration in free-fall

All **friction** forces act in the opposite direction to the direction of motion and slow an object down. There are ways of reducing friction forces.

- Friction forces between moving parts of a machine can be reduced by **lubricating** (oiling) them.
- Friction forces on moving objects such as vehicles can be reduced by **streamlining** their shapes in the following ways:
  - shaping car roof boxes
  - making high-speed cars wedge-like in shape
  - angling lorry deflectors.

FIGURE 5: The shapes of the car roof box and the lorry deflector help to streamline the vehicles. What advantage does streamlining give to vehicles?

DID YOU KNOW?

On the Moon and in outer Space there is no drag because there is no atmosphere.

Streamlining is designed to reduce the drag force acting on a vehicle, which allows its top speed to increase. Air passes over a streamlined vehicle more easily than if it had sharp corners and a square shape.

> **QUESTIONS**
>
> 6 Would the top speed of a car be greater or less without a roof box?
> 7 Suggest why dolphins and sharks have a streamlined shape.

...friction

Falling objects

In general all objects fall with the same acceleration.

But this is only true if the effect of air resistance is very small.

When falling towards Earth through the atmosphere there is always a drag force (air resistance) as the falling object displaces air molecules.

The size of the air resistance force on a falling object depends on:

■ its cross-sectional area – the larger the area the greater the air resistance

■ its speed – the faster it falls the greater the air resistance.

Air resistance only has a significant effect on motion when it is large compared to the weight of the falling object.

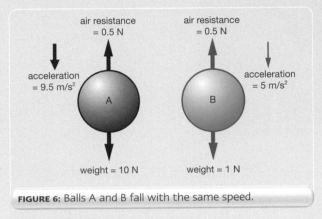

FIGURE 6: Balls A and B fall with the same speed.

Free-fall

A true free-falling object falls under the influence of gravity only.

■ Free-falling objects do not experience air resistance.

■ Free-falling objects, irrespective of mass or shape, accelerate downwards at the same rate.

Examples of free-fall are:

■ objects falling above Earth's atmosphere

■ objects falling on the Moon

■ the Moon itself.

The Moon is in free-fall towards Earth. It is falling with an acceleration that is equal to gravity, g, at the height of its orbit (about 0.003 m/s^2). It never gets closer to Earth because of Earth's curvature.

FIGURE 7: The Moon and Earth. Why does the Moon not get closer to Earth?

QUESTIONS

8 Estimate the force with which Earth attracts each kilogram of the Moon.

9 Explain why free-fall parachutists are not actually in free-fall unless they jump from an aeroplane at a very high altitude.

10 Use the equation $F=ma$ to check that the values given for the acceleration of A and B in Figure 6 are correct.

The energy of games and theme rides

You will find out:

- about gravitational potential energy
- how there is a transfer of gravitational potential energy to kinetic energy as an object falls
- how to calculate gravitational potential energy

Let the force be with you!

The rides at theme parks are designed to thrill and frighten people! They cause rapid energy changes that distort a person's 'gravity'. People on the rides experience G-forces similar to those experienced by astronauts on lift-off. Roller coasters can be quite gentle or terrifying, depending on the steepness of the track – and a person's 'scare factor'!

Gravitational potential energy

An object held above the ground has **gravitational potential energy**. The amount of gravitational potential energy an object has depends on:

- its **mass**
- its height above the ground.

The vertical-drop roller coaster shown starts with a 60 m climb (to gain gravitational potential energy) and then is stationary for 3 seconds hanging over the edge of a 60 m vertical drop. After being released each carriage reaches a speed of 110 km/h and the people in the carriage experience a force of 4.5 G. (This means a person feels 4.5 times their normal weight.)

FIGURE 1: A vertical-drop roller coaster. Why does the roller coaster start with a climb to the top?

DID YOU KNOW?

The world's first vertical-drop roller coaster called 'Oblivion' opened in 1998 at Alton Towers, Staffordshire.

▮▮ QUESTIONS ▮▮

1. What sort of energy do the riders possess waiting at the top of a roller coaster?

2. Sam and his dad are riding on 'Oblivion'. Who has the greater gravitational potential energy when they are held at the top of the drop?

...air resistance ...efficiency ...gravitational potential energy ...kinetic energy

Energy transfers

The riders at the top of a roller coaster ride have a lot of gravitational potential energy.

The gravitational potential energy is quickly changed to **kinetic energy** as the carriages descend.

A person on a swing experiences the following energy changes:

- gravitational potential energy at the top of the swing
- changes to kinetic energy at the bottom of the swing
- which changes to gravitational potential energy at the top again.

FIGURE 2: A person swinging experiences constant changes in energy. What two forms of energy are involved?

A bouncing ball converts gravitational potential energy to kinetic energy and back to gravitational potential energy.

If a ball is dropped from a height of 2 m it does not return to its original height because energy is transferred to other forms such as **thermal energy** and **sound energy**.

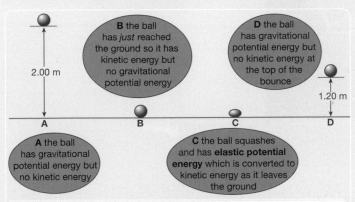

B the ball has *just* reached the ground so it has kinetic energy but no gravitational potential energy

D the ball has gravitational potential energy but no kinetic energy at the top of the bounce

2.00 m

1.20 m

A   B   C   D

A the ball has gravitational potential energy but no kinetic energy

C the ball squashes and has **elastic potential energy** which is converted to kinetic energy as it leaves the ground

FIGURE 3: Stages of energy transfer when a ball is dropped. The gravitational potential energy at **D** is less than the gravitational potential energy at **A**.

▒▒▒▒ **QUESTIONS** ▒▒▒▒

3 Describe the main energy change that takes place when the riders on 'Oblivion' drop vertically.

4 Look at Figure 3.

  a What types of energy does the bouncing ball possess when it is 1 m above the ground?

  b Suggest why the gravitational potential energy of the ball at **D** is less than its gravitational potential energy at **A**.

Calculating gravitational potential energy

To calculate the gravitational potential energy (GPE) of an object the following equation is used:

GPE = mgh

where m = mass in kg

  h = vertical height moved in m

  g = gravitational field strength in N/kg (on Earth, g = 10 N/kg)

If the ball in Figure 3 of mass 50 g is dropped from a height **A** of 2 m and bounces up to a height **D** of 1.2 m, the energy wasted in the bounce is:

gravitational potential energy lost between **A** and **D** = mgh

= 0.05 × 10 × (2.00 − 1.20) = 0.4 J

The initial gravitational potential energy is 1.0 J, so 40% of the ball's energy is wasted. The energy **efficiency** of the bounce is 60%.

Energy and terminal velocity

Velocity is speed in a known direction.

When a skydiver reaches **terminal velocity** their kinetic energy ($\frac{1}{2} mv^2$) has a maximum value and remains constant. The gravitational potential energy lost as they fall is used to do **work** against friction (**air resistance**).

When terminal velocity is reached:

FIGURE 4: When a skydiver reaches terminal velocity, what happens to their kinetic energy?

change in gravitational potential energy = work done against friction

▒▒▒▒ **QUESTIONS** ▒▒▒▒

5 The skydiver in Figure 4 is in a streamlined position. How could he slow down?

6 A ski jumper of mass 70 kg is at the top of a 120 m jump.
Calculate his gravitational potential energy.

Water-powered funicular railway

A water-powered **funicular railway** has a carriage that takes on water at the top of the hill giving it extra gravitational potential energy.

As the carriage travels down the hillside it transfers gravitational potential energy to kinetic energy and pulls up another carriage with an empty water tank on a parallel rail.

FIGURE 5: The water-powered Lynton and Lynmouth funicular railway.

You will find out:

- more about gravitational potential energy and kinetic energy
- how a roller coaster works
- how to change the subject of the equation for gravitational potential energy

Kinetic energy

A moving object has kinetic energy. The amount of kinetic energy an object has depends on:

- its mass
- its speed (how fast it is moving).

FIGURE 6: Compared to a horse standing still, the horses here have more kinetic energy. The ploughing horses have more mass and thus more kinetic energy. The racehorses are moving faster so have more kinetic energy.

QUESTIONS

7 Give **two** ways of increasing the gravitational potential energy of an object.

8 Give **two** ways of increasing the kinetic energy of an object.

...conservation of energy   ...funicular railway

How a roller coaster works

FIGURE 7: What type of energy is the leading train gaining on this roller coaster?

A traditional roller coaster works by using a motor to haul a train up in the air, giving it a lot of gravitational potential energy. The train is then released, converting gravitational potential energy to kinetic energy as it falls. Each peak is lower than the one before because some energy is transferred to heat and sound due to friction and air resistance.

The principle of **conservation of energy** tells us that:

gravitational potential energy at top	=	kinetic energy at bottom	+	energy transferred (to heat and sound) due to friction

- At the peaks the train has a lot of gravitational potential energy (high up) and little kinetic energy (moves slowly).
- At the bottom the train has little gravitational potential energy (low down) and a lot of kinetic energy (moves fast).

Speed of a roller coaster

The more gravitational potential energy gained by the roller coaster, the greater its maximum speed.

$$\text{kinetic energy} = \frac{1}{2}mv^2$$

Ignoring friction, as the train falls:

- loss of gravitational potential energy = gain in kinetic energy = $\frac{1}{2}mv^2$
- if the gravitational potential energy is doubled, the kinetic energy doubles
- if the kinetic energy doubles the speed increases but does not double (it increases by $\sqrt{2}$).

Relationship of speed and kinetic energy

- If speed doubles, kinetic energy quadruples (kinetic energy $\propto v^2$).
- If mass doubles, kinetic energy doubles (kinetic energy $\propto m$).

QUESTIONS

9 Why do the heights of the peaks on roller coaster rides decrease progressively?

10 On long roller coaster rides the trains are given a short lift by a motor part-way through the ride. Why is this done?

Mass and weight

The force of attraction on a mass due to gravity is called **weight**.

> force, (F) = mass, (m) × acceleration, (a)

When falling freely $a = g$, the acceleration due to **gravity** and:

> weight, $W = mg$

The weight of an object is found by multiplying its mass by g.
On Earth, $g = 10$ N/kg.

example

Sadaf has a mass of 54 kg.

She weighs 54 × 10 = 540 N on Earth.

Gravity applies a force of 10 N to each kilogram of mass on Earth.

Sadaf only weighs 90 N on the Moon.

This means **gravitational field strength** on the Moon is less than on Earth.

$$W = mg \quad \text{so } g = \frac{W}{m} = \frac{90}{54} = 1.6 \text{ N/kg}$$

 Don't confuse mass (in kg) and weight (in N).

QUESTIONS

11 A Moon buggy has a mass of 10 kg. Find its weight:

   a on Earth

   b on the Moon.

12 Tom weighs 720 N on Earth and 1080 N on the newly discovered planet Zeus. What is the gravitational field strength on Zeus?

Module summary

Concept map

Distance-time graphs

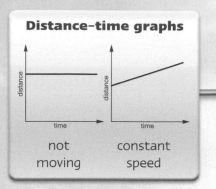

not moving   constant speed

Speed and acceleration

$$speed = \frac{distance}{time}$$

$$acceleration = \frac{change\ in\ speed}{time}$$

Speed-time graphs

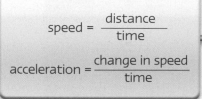

constant speed   increasing speed

Force, mass and acceleration are linked by the equation: $F = ma$

Forces and motion

Forces can make things speed up or slow down.

When a car stops, the total stopping distance =

thinking distance + braking distance

The higher the speed of the car, the greater the distance it travels in stopping.

Pairs of forces

Forces always occur in pairs that are the same size, act in opposite directions and act on different objects.

Work is done when a force moves an object. $W = F \times d$

Work is measured in joules (J).

Work, energy and power

Moving objects possess kinetic energy. The faster they travel, the more kinetic energy they possess. The greater the mass of an object, the more kinetic energy it possesses.

kinetic energy (KE) = $\frac{1}{2}mv^2$

Energy is needed to do work. Energy is measured in joules (J).

Power is a measure of how quickly work is done.
Power is measured in watts (W). $P = \frac{W}{t}$

Roller coasters use gravitational potential energy as the source of movement.

Modern cars have safety features that absorb energy when the cars stop.

Terminal speed

This is the maximum speed reached by a falling object. It happens when the forces acting on the object are balanced.

Falling safely

Falling objects get faster as they fall. They are pulled towards the centre of the Earth by their weight (gravity).

A parachute provides a large upward force, bigger than the weight of the parachutist. This slows him down. As he slows down the air resistance gets less until it equals his weight. He then falls at a low terminal speed and lands safely.

Module quiz

1   Write down the equation that links speed, distance and time.

2   What is 'acceleration' and what unit is it usually measured in?

3   What quantity is found from the gradient of a distance–time graph?

4   What quantity is found from the gradient of a speed–time graph?

5   What quantity is found from the area under a speed–time graph?

6   A car accelerates from 0 m/s to 20 m/s in 8 seconds. Calculate its acceleration.

7   Write down the equation linking the resultant force on an object with its mass and acceleration.

8   Two ice skaters collide. Write down **two** facts about the forces acting on the two skaters.

9   What is meant by 'thinking time'?

10 How do you calculate the total stopping distance of a car?

11 How do you calculate the work done by a force and what unit is it measured in?

12 Anya lifts a 40 N box 2.5 m in 8 seconds. Tal lifts a 50 N box 2 m in 12 seconds. Who is more powerful?

13 What is meant by kinetic energy?

14 Why do crumple zones reduce the risk of injury in a car accident?

15 Give **two** examples of passive safety features in a car.

16 Ben drops a ball. What is its acceleration?

17 Which has the more streamlined shape, a Land Rover car or a sports car?

18 The Moon is in free-fall towards the Earth. If it is falling, why does it never get any closer?

19 Give **two** ways of increasing the gravitational potential energy of an object.

20 Why is each peak of a roller coaster track lower than the one before?

Numeracy activity

The graph shows the motion of a free-fall parachutist.

QUESTIONS

1   Between which points on the graph was the parachutist falling at a constant speed?

2   At which point did her parachute open?

3   Name the **two** main forces acting on the parachutist between A and B.

4   Between which two points was the air resistance force greater than the weight of the parachutist?

5   Why does a parachutist spread out her arms and legs as she falls?

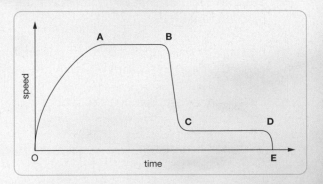

Exam practice

Exam practice questions

1   **a**   The graph below shows a velocity-time graph for two cars, called Racer and Whiz. They are undergoing tests.

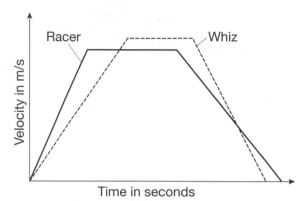

     i   Describe the motion of Racer.   [3]

     ii   State which car, Racer or Whiz, travelled fastest.   [1]

   b   The following table shows information about the two cars.

	Racer	Whiz
Top speed	38 m/s	40 m/s
Time to reach top speed	5 seconds	7 seconds
Mass	700 kg	650 kg

     i   Calculate which car accelerates more quickly.   [4]

     ii   What force is required to stop Whiz in 4 seconds when it is travelling at an initial speed of 25 m/s?   [3]

   c   State two factors that could affect the driver's reaction time.   [2]

   d   Explain why the stopping distance does not depend only on the driver's reaction time.   [2]

   e   Explain how a seatbelt helps to reduce injury if the car crashes.   [2]

[Total 17 marks]

2   A falling raindrop reaches a maximum speed.

   a   Explain, in terms of forces, why the raindrop does not keep accelerating as it falls.   [4]

   b   State, with one reason, whether a larger raindrop will reach a faster maximum speed.   [2]

   c   What is the kinetic energy of one drop with a mass of 0.1 g which falls at 3 m/s?   [3]

[Total 9 marks]

3   A conveyor belt in a factory carries bags of flour to be packaged. Each bag has a mass of 1.5 kg.

   a   State the weight of each bag of flour.   [2]

   b   Calculate the work done as each pallet containing 12 bags is lifted through a height of 1.2 m onto the conveyor belt.   [4]

   c   The conveyor belt travels at a speed of 1 m/s. How much kinetic energy does each bag of flour have as it travels along the belt?   [4]

   d   If the conveyor belt is put onto a faster setting, more energy is wasted.
Give one reason why the conveyor belt wastes more energy when it is going faster.   [2]

[Total 12 marks]

4   Johann has bought an electric car as he believes it does not pollute the environment.

   a   Where is the electrical energy used to recharge the battery produced?   [1]

   b   Does using an electric car produce pollution? Explain your answer.   [3]

   c   To drive the car economically, Johann has been told not to drive faster than 90 km per hour. Give one other way in which Johann could drive his car more economically. Explain your answer.   [2]

[Total 6 marks]

A roller coaster uses a motor to pull its cars up to a start point. Initially it stops, and then it releases and travels along the track using no further energy input.

a Explain in terms of energy why the start point is the highest point. [3]

b Explain where the cars travel fastest on the ride. [2]

c How much work is done when the motor raises one car of mass 200 kg through a height of 60 m? [3]

Correct but not enough for this answer. The motor only supplies energy at the start so this is where the car's energy is at a maximum. The car is not moving so it only has GPE at the start. Its GPE depends on height only as its mass is constant.

a *As the car goes up and down gravitational potential energy is changed into kinetic energy. Gravitational potential energy depends on height.*

b *The car travels fastest at the lowest point because most gravitational potential energy has been changed into kinetic energy.*

Correct – the student has explained their answer fully and so has been awarded the full two marks.

c *work done = force × distance =*
200 × 60 = 12 000 J

Incorrect. The student has used the correct formula to calculate work done but has forgotten to change mass (in kg) into weight (in N) by multiplying by 10. They should have used '2000' in their calculation, giving an answer of 120 000 J or 120 kJ.

Overall Grade: C

How to get an A

It is important to recognise where an examiner wants a fuller answer (as in a). Use the mark scheme as a guide to how much you should write. Make sure that you have put down a point for each mark – and never leave blank spaces!

This X-ray shows a healthy human gall bladder. Sometimes gall stones can develop in the gall bladder and bile ducts. Ultrasound can be used to break down these stones.

This endoscope has been used to inject a material into the small intestine. The material absorbs X-rays, giving us the image we see here.

Advances in medical physics have enabled us to make huge strides in the diagnosis and treatment of many diseases. Development in the fields of nuclear physics and waves, such as X-rays and ultrasound, coupled with the rapid rise of computer technology, is improving our quality of life and extending our life expectancy.

Ultrasound is a longitudinal wave. It can also be used for scanning the body. Unlike X-rays, ultrasound does not damage living cells.

X-rays are electromagnetic waves. They are made by firing high speed electrons at metal targets.

CONTENTS

Sparks!

You will find out:
- how insulating materials can become charged
- how charged objects can attract other objects
- that there are two types of electric charge
- about electron movement

Lightning strikes

Lightning occurs when a cloud becomes charged and an electric current passes between the cloud and Earth.

Static electric charges can build up on insulating materials. These charges can cause electric shocks or explosions.

Cloud to ground lightning striking a mountain peak.

Insulating materials

Metals are good electrical **conductors**. They allow **electric charges** to move through them.

Materials such as wood, glass and polythene are **insulators**. They do not allow electric charges to pass through them.

Charge can build up on an insulator. An insulator can be charged by **friction**.

If a polythene rod is charged by rubbing it with a duster it **attracts** small pieces of paper. Other materials can be charged by friction:

- when a balloon is rubbed on a sweater it becomes charged and sticks to the wall
- when a plastic comb is used to comb hair both the comb and hair can become charged
- some types of dusting brushes are designed to become charged and attract dust.

There are two kinds of electric charge, **positive** and **negative**. When rubbed with a duster:

- acetate and perspex become positively charged
- polythene becomes negatively charged.

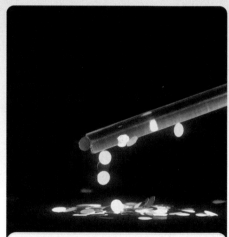

FIGURE 1: A polythene rod becomes charged by friction and attracts discs of paper.

▮▮ QUESTIONS ▮▮

1 Which **one** of the following is not an insulator?
   candle wax   glass   iron   rubber   wood
2 Explain why static charges do not build up on a conductor.

...atom   ...attract   ...conductor   ...electric charge   ...electron   ...electrostatic

Positive and negative charges

An **atom** is a small positively charged nucleus surrounded by negatively charged **electrons**. In a stable, neutral atom, there are the same amounts of positive and negative charges.

All **electrostatic** effects are caused by the movement of electrons.

The law of electric charge states that like charges **repel** and unlike charges attract.

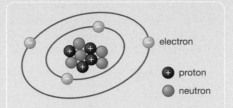

FIGURE 2: The charges in a neutral atom balance. This atom has four electrons. How many protons does it have?

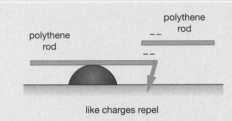

FIGURE 3: Like charges repel and unlike charges attract.

Van de Graaff generator

A Van de Graaff generator collects electric charge on a metal dome.

- A person places their hands on the dome when it is uncharged.
- The dome is switched on and it and the person become charged.
- All the person's hairs gain the same charge.
- Like charges repel, so the hairs move away from each other.

 It is only electrons that move in an atom.

FIGURE 4: When the girl puts her hands on the Van de Graaff generator she becomes charged. Why does her hair stand on end?

Moving electrons

- When a polythene rod is rubbed with a duster electrons are transferred from the duster to the polythene, making the polythene rod negatively charged.

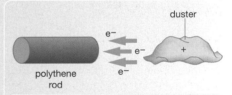

FIGURE 5: Why does the polythene rod become negatively charged when it is rubbed with a duster?

- When an acetate rod is rubbed with a duster electrons are transferred from the acetate to the duster, leaving the acetate rod positively charged.

In general an object has:

- a negative charge due to an excess of electrons
- a positive charge due to a lack of electrons.

QUESTIONS

3 Copy and complete the table.

+	–	attract
+	+	
–	–	
–	+	

4 a A neutral carbon atom has six protons in its nucleus. How many electrons does it have?

b What happens to make it a positive ion?

QUESTIONS

5 A polythene rod is charged by rubbing it with a duster. What charge, if any, does the duster gain?

6 What happens if a conductor becomes positively charged?

7 Explain why when Gina pulls her woolly hat off very quickly her hair stands on end.

Electric shocks

A person gets an **electrostatic shock** if they become charged and then become **earthed**.

For example, a person can become charged if they walk on a nylon carpet or vinyl floor because:

- the floor is an insulator
- they become charged as they walk due to friction.

The person can become earthed by touching water pipes or even another person.

FIGURE 6: Birds sitting on high-voltage power lines. Can you suggest why they do not get an electric shock?

You will find out:

- how you can get an electrostatic shock
- how static electricity can be dangerous
- how to reduce the chance of getting an electric shock

DID YOU KNOW?

A microscopic coating of oil prevents 'frictional charging'.

QUESTIONS

8 Jake got an electric shock when he touched the car door after a journey. How did the car become charged?

9 Why can a person become earthed by touching water pipes?

...current   ...earthed   ...electrostatic shock

When static electricity is dangerous

Static electricity is dangerous in conditions where there are explosive materials.

When inflammable gases or vapours are present or there is a high concentration of oxygen, a spark from static electricity could ignite the gases or vapours and cause an explosion.

- When cleaning oil tankers their tanks are first filled with an inert gas such as nitrogen to avoid a spark that could cause an explosion.

- Mobile telephones must not be used on petrol station forecourts to prevent sparks that could cause an explosion.

FIGURE 7: How are explosions prevented in the tanks of oil tankers during cleaning?

If a person touches something at a high **voltage**, large amounts of electric charge may flow through their body to earth.

Current is the rate of flow of charge. The table shows that even small currents can be fatal.

The voltage that produces a given current depends on the **resistance**. The resistance of the body varies.

If a person is barefoot and sweaty, resistance is low and the current is greater for a given voltage.

Electric current in mA (contact time is 1 second)	Effect on the body
1	tingling sensation
10–20	'can't let go!', muscles keep contracting
100–300	**ventricular fibrillation** (heart attack), fatal in some cases

When static electricity is a nuisance

There are times when static electricity is a nuisance but not dangerous.

- Dust and dirt are attracted to insulators, such as a television screen.

- Clothes made from synthetic materials often 'cling' to each other and to the body.

FIGURE 8: Factory workers in Vietnam assembling television and stereo parts. Can you suggest why they wear a wristband to discharge static electricity?

10 Why are high oxygen levels dangerous in a situation where electric charges are allowed to build up?

11 Explain why clothes made from synthetic materials may 'cling'.

Safety measures

Electric shocks can be avoided in the following ways.

- If an object that is likely to become charged is connected to earth, any build up of charge immediately flows down the earth wire.

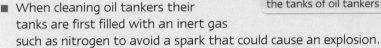

FIGURE 9: Lorries containing inflammable gases and liquids are always earthed before they are unloaded. This prevents a spark igniting the gas or liquid.

- In a factory where machinery is at risk of becoming charged, the operators stand on insulating rubber mats so that charge cannot flow through them to earth.

- Shoes with insulating soles are worn by workers if there is a risk of charge building up so that charge cannot flow through them to earth.

Anti-static devices

- Sprays, liquids and dusters made from conducting materials carry away electric charge. This prevents a build up of charge that could be dangerous or a nuisance.

- 'Dryer sheets' containing oil are used in tumble dryers to prevent static charging.

12 Explain why aircraft tyres are made from a type of rubber that conducts electricity.

13 Why is there a risk of static charge building up in a factory using machinery?

Uses of electrostatics

You will find out:

- about some uses of electrostatics
- how a defibrillator can be used to restart a person's heart

Missing a beat...

Static electricity can be a nuisance but it can also be of potential benefit to us all.

When a person suffers a heart attack their heart stops beating. A defibrillator uses static electricity to restart their heart. It is a procedure that does not always work but it has saved many lives.

Portable and implanted defibrillators allow a more rapid response and help to save even more lives.

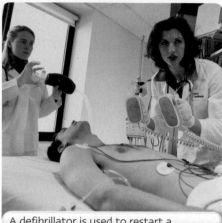

A defibrillator is used to restart a patient's heart.

Uses of static electricity

There are many uses of **static electricity**.

- A paint sprayer **charges** paint droplets to give an even coverage.
- A photocopier and laser printer use charged particles to produce an image.
- Charged plates inside factory chimneys are used to remove dust particles from smoke.
- A **defibrillator** delivers a controlled electric shock through a patient's chest to restart their heart.

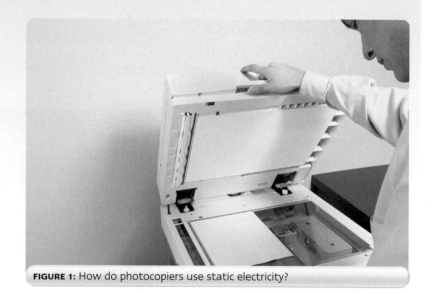

FIGURE 1: How do photocopiers use static electricity?

⊪ QUESTIONS ⊪

1   Why do paint sprayers charge paint droplets?
2   Give **two** other uses of static electricity.
3   What is a defibrillator used for?

...charge   ...defibrillator   ...energy   ...heart rhythm

What does a defibrillator do?

Defibrillation is a procedure that restores a regular **heart rhythm** by delivering an electric shock through the chest wall to the heart. Once the heart resumes its pumping action, blood can once more flow throughout the body.

- Two **paddles** are charged from a high-voltage supply.
- They are then placed firmly on the patient's chest to ensure a good electrical contact.
- Electric charge is passed through the patient to make their heart contract. Once the heart has been artificially restarted it is hoped that it will continue to contract normally.
- Great care is taken to ensure that the operator does not receive an electric shock.

FIGURE 2: Paddles on a defibrillator. What are they used for?

Portable defibrillators for home use

Rapid treatment is essential if defibrillation is to be successful. Up to 80 000 people die in the UK each year due to sudden cardiac arrest, with 80 per cent of such incidents happening at home. The chances of surviving decrease by 10 per cent for each minute that passes before treatment is received.

In recent years, small portable machines have been developed for use in the home.

FIGURE 3: A portable defibrillator. How does this machine help to save lives?

More on a defibrillator

A typical shock from a defibrillator supplies about 400 J of **energy** in a few milliseconds (1 millisecond = 0.001 seconds).

If a defibrillator is switched on for 5 milliseconds (0.005 seconds), the **power** can be calculated from:

$$\text{power} = \frac{\text{energy}}{\text{time}} = \frac{400}{0.005} = 80\,000\text{ W}$$

An implantable cardiac defibrillator

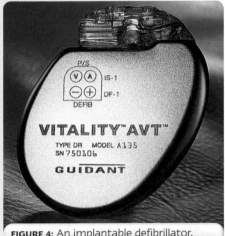

FIGURE 4: An implantable defibrillator. What is its main advantage?

An implantable defibrillator is a small (6 × 6 × 1.5 cm) battery-powered device. It is implanted under the skin in the upper part of the chest wall and is connected to the heart. It monitors heart rhythm and **senses** if there is about to be a severe disturbance in heart rhythm. If necessary it delivers an electrical impulse to the heart to stop abnormal rhythm and allow normal rhythm to resume. It can deliver up to four consecutive discharges of 25 to 30 J.

QUESTIONS

6 Why is everyone warned to "stand clear!" before a defibrillator is used?

7 Suggest why a larger current than those referred to in the table on page 217 can be used in a defibrillator.

8 What is **one** disadvantage of an implanted defibrillator?

QUESTIONS

4 How could the current through a patient be increased in defibrillation?

5 A defibrillator passes 96 mC (0.096 C) of charge through a patient in 2 ms (0.002 seconds). What is the average current through the patient?

You will find out:

- about the application of electrostatics to paint spraying
- how electrostatic dust precipitators work

Paint spraying

- The spray gun is charged.
- All the paint particles become charged with the same charge.
- Like charges **repel** and the paint particles spread out giving a fine spray.
- The object to be painted is given the opposite charge to the paint.
- Opposite charges **attract** and the paint is attracted to the object and sticks to it.

FIGURE 5: Paint spraying. What are the advantages of using electrostatic paint sprayers?

The advantages of electrostatic paint sprayers are:

- reduction in wasted paint
- an object receives an even coat of paint
- paint covers awkward places ('shadows').

Electrostatic dust precipitators

Gases lost from the chimneys of many factories and power stations contain harmful particles that **pollute** the atmosphere. A **dust precipitator** is used to remove harmful smoke particles from a chimney.

- A metal grid (or wires) is placed in the chimney.
- The grid is connected to a high-voltage supply.
- Dust particles are attracted to the metal grid.
- The dust particles stick together to form larger particles.
- When these particles are large enough they fall down the chimney and are used to make building blocks.

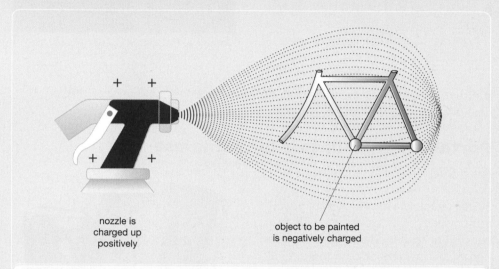

nozzle is charged up positively

object to be painted is negatively charged

FIGURE 6: How an electrostatic paint sprayer works.

FIGURE 7: Smoke escaping from chimneys. How is this smoke cleaned using electrostatics?

QUESTIONS

9 A similar method to a dust precipitator is used for fingerprinting. Paper is put near a charged wire. A black powder is used in place of smoke. Suggest how it works.

10 Write down **two** possible consequences of not using electrostatic dust precipitators in an industrial area with lots of chimneys.

11 When disinfectant is sprayed on an area, the droplets of disinfectant are sometimes given a positive charge by a spray gun. Suggest why this is done.

...attract   ...dust precipitator

More on paint spraying

If the object to be painted is not charged the paint moves on to it, but:

- the object becomes charged from the paint, gaining the same charge
- further paint droplets are repelled away from the object.

This can be avoided by earthing an object to prevent a build up of charge.

The above method can be used when painting small objects but on the production line of a factory or in a vehicle-repair shop electrostatic paint sprayers are used. The objects to be painted are charged with the opposite charge to the paint.

FIGURE 8: Crop sprayers work in a similar way to paint sprayers to give a large even cloud of pesticide.

More on dust precipitators

Some power stations burn coal to produce electricity. The smoke from their chimneys must be cleaned before it is released into the air.

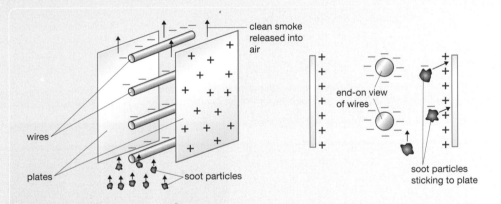

FIGURE 10: How a dust precipitator works.

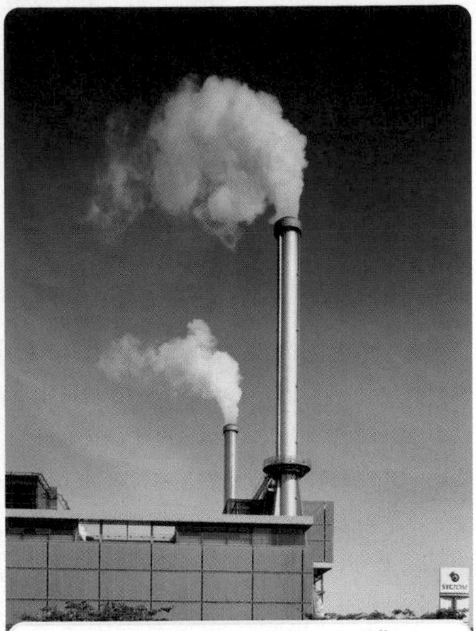

FIGURE 9: Drax power station at Selby, Yorkshire, has a main chimney 259 m high that produces a lot of soot which must be removed.

- A dust precipitator inside a chimney contains wires in a grid that are given a large negative charge.
- As the soot particles pass close to the wires the soot particles become negatively charged.
- Like charges repel and the soot particles are repelled away from the wires and attracted to the positively charged plates.
- The soot particles stick to the plates and are removed at intervals.

QUESTIONS

12 Explain why paint spreads out into a fine spray from the nozzle of a spray gun.

13 Explain what would happen if the wires in a dust precipitator were positively charged and the metal plates negatively charged.

14 Suggest how a crop sprayer produces an even cloud of pesticide.

...pollute ...repel

Safe electricals

You will find out:
- about the behaviour of simple circuits
- what carry the charge in a circuit
- about the relationship between current, potential difference and resistance

Electricity is important in our lives

People use electrical appliances, from computers to washing machines, every day but they often forget that electricity can be dangerous if not used correctly.

A modern domestic wiring system that includes fuses and circuit breakers is designed to protect people and property if an electrical fault occurs.

In the UK, more than 28 000 fires a year are caused by electrical faults, leading to over 2500 deaths or serious injuries.

Incorrect wiring in electrical appliances can lead to fire.

Electric circuits

A closed loop, with no gaps, is required for a **circuit** to work.

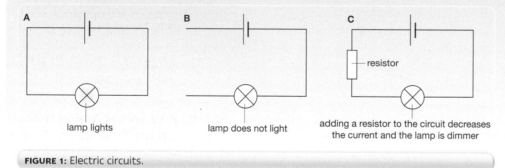

A — lamp lights

B — lamp does not light

C — resistor — adding a resistor to the circuit decreases the current and the lamp is dimmer

FIGURE 1: Electric circuits.

A **resistor** is added to a circuit to change the amount of **current** in it.

FIGURE 2: Carbon resistors. What does a resistor do when it is connected in an electric circuit?

QUESTIONS

1 In Figure 1, which of the circuits, **A**, **B** or **C**, has:
   a the largest current
   b the smallest current?
2 How could the lamp in Figure 1 be made brighter?

...ammeter ...ampere ...charge ...circuit ...current ...electron
...filament ...ohm ...parallel

Electric current

An electric current is a flow of electric **charge**.

In an electric circuit, charge is carried by negatively charged **electrons** in metal atoms. The electrons are free to move and flow in the opposite direction to the conventional current.

If a circuit has a large resistance it is hard for the charge to move. In this case the rate of flow of charge (or current) is small.

A **variable resistor** (or **rheostat**) can be used to change the resistance and current in a circuit.

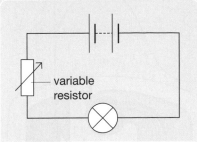

FIGURE 3: This circuit has a variable resistor and acts as a dimmer switch.

The current in a circuit is measured in **amperes** (A) using an **ammeter**. An ammeter is connected in **series**.

Potential difference

The **potential difference** (pd) between two points in a circuit is the difference in **voltage** between the two points.

Potential difference is measured in **volts** (V) using a **voltmeter**.

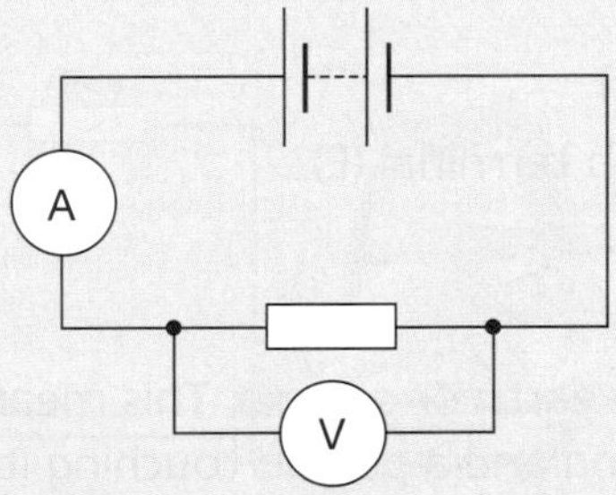

A voltmeter is always connected in **parallel**.

- For a fixed resistor, as the pd across it increases, the current increases.
- For a fixed power supply, as the resistance increases, the current decreases.

$$\text{resistance} = \frac{\text{potential difference}}{\text{current}} = \frac{V}{I} \quad \text{where the unit is } \textbf{ohm } (\Omega)$$

example

In the circuit in Figure 5 the voltmeter reads 5.0 V and the ammeter reads 0.2 A:

$$\text{resistance of the lamp, } R = \frac{V}{I} = \frac{5.0}{0.2} = 25\,\Omega$$

FIGURE 4: Measuring the potential difference across a resistor using a voltmeter. Is a voltmeter connected in series or parallel?

▨▨▨ QUESTIONS ▨▨▨

3 Explain how a variable resistor acts as a dimmer switch varying the brightness of a lamp.

4 The potential difference across a resistor is 12 V and the current is 0.6 A. What is the value of its resistance?

Linking resistance, potential difference and current

$$\text{Resistance, } R = \frac{\text{pd}}{\text{current}} = \frac{V}{I}$$

$$\text{So, } V = IR \text{ and } I = \frac{V}{R}$$

example

A piece of wire has a resistance of 3 Ω and melts if the current through it exceeds 5 A.

The maximum pd across the wire, V, possible without melting the wire is:

$$V = IR = 5 \times 3 = 15\,\text{V}.$$

Current in a circuit

The current in a circuit must not be allowed to get too high.

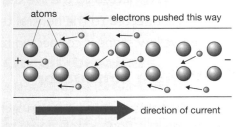

FIGURE 5: The movement of electrons in a wire carrying a current.

- Electrons are 'pushed' around a circuit by the battery. They bump into the atoms in the resistor. This makes the atoms vibrate more so the resistor gets hotter.

- The increased atomic vibrations impede the electrons' motion more so the resistance increases.

- The **filament** in a lamp connected in a circuit becomes so hot it emits light.

▨▨▨ QUESTIONS ▨▨▨

5 What is the pd across a 6 Ω resistor when the current in it is 1.5 A?

6 What current passes through a 4 Ω resistor when the pd across it is 12 V?

...*potential difference* ...*resistor* ...*rheostat* ...*series* ...*variable resistor*
...*volt* ...*voltage* ...*voltmeter*

Uses of ultrasound

Ultrasound allows a doctor to 'see' inside a patient without surgery.

You will find out:

- how ultrasound is used in medicine
- about the reasons for using ultrasound rather than X-rays

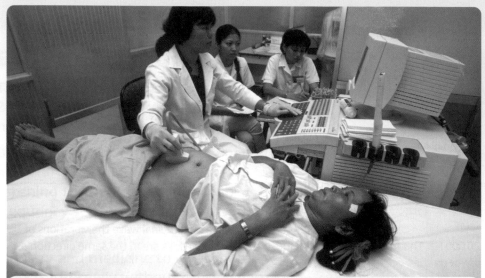

FIGURE 7: An ultrasound scan being carried out on a pregnant woman. The image of the uterus and foetus is shown on the computer screen. The technician checks for abnormalities in growth and development of the foetus.

Uses of ultrasound **scans** include:

- to check the condition of a foetus
- to investigate heart and liver problems
- to look for tumours in the body
- to break down kidney stones and stones elsewhere in the body

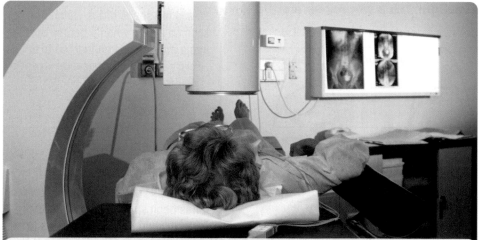

FIGURE 8: A patient undergoing ultrasound treatment to break down kidney stones. What is the main advantage of this approach?

- to measure the speed of blood flow in vessels when a blockage of a vein or artery is suspected.

QUESTIONS

7 Give **two** uses of ultrasound scanning.

8 Explain how ultrasound is used to clean jewellery.

...body scan   ...cataract   ...echo   ...gel   ...image

Using ultrasound in a body scan

An ultrasound **body scan** is used to establish the exact position of a problem in a patient, making surgery easier.

A **pulse** of ultrasound is sent into a patient's body. At each boundary between different tissues or organs some ultrasound is **reflected** and the rest is transmitted. The returning **echoes** are recorded and used to build up an **image** of the internal structure.

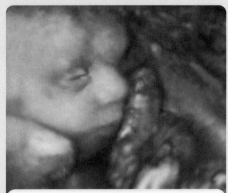

FIGURE 9: Coloured image of a 3-D ultrasound scan of the face of a foetus at approximately 25 weeks gestation. What is the advantage of 3-D scanning compared to 2-D scanning?

Foetal ultrasound scanning is routine during pregnancy. A three-dimensional (3-D) scan uses computer technology and gives a more detailed image than a conventional two-dimensional (2-D) scan.

A **gel** is placed on a patient's body between the ultrasound probe and their skin. Without gel virtually all the ultrasound would be reflected at the skin and a good image of internal structure would not be obtained.

Using ultrasound to break down kidney stones

A high-powered ultrasound beam is used to break down kidney and other stones inside the body. Even large stones can be broken down into fragments that are then excreted from the body in the normal way. Before this stones required major surgery.

Cataract surgery

A surgeon uses ultrasound to break up the opaque lens of a patient suffering a **cataract** (loss of transparency in the lens of the eye). To restore normal vision, the defective lens is surgically removed and replaced by an artificial one.

QUESTIONS

9 Why is a high-powered ultrasound beam needed to break down kidney stones?

10 Suggest why a pregnant woman is scanned using ultrasound but is never X-rayed.

How a body scan works

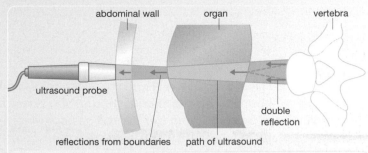

FIGURE 10: How ultrasound is reflected during a body scan. What does the proportion of ultrasound reflected at a tissue boundary depend on?

When ultrasound is reflected from different **interfaces** in the body, the depth of each structure is calculated using:

$$\text{speed} = \frac{\text{distance}}{\text{time}}$$

given the standard speed of ultrasound for different tissue types

The proportion of ultrasound reflected at each interface depends on:

■ the densities of the adjoining tissues
■ the speed of sound in the adjoining tissues.

If the tissues are very different (for example blood and bone) most of the ultrasound is reflected, leaving very little to penetrate further into the body.

Doppler ultrasound scanner

This probe detects movement. It is held against an artery or a pregnant woman's abdomen. If ultrasound waves hit a moving object the frequency of the echoes alters. This allows speed of blood flow or foetal heart rate to be measured.

Advantages of ultrasound compared to X-rays

■ Ultrasound differentiates between soft tissues better than **X-rays**. X-rays show bones very well.

■ Ultrasound does not damage living cells. X-rays can kill cells or bring about changes in them that can lead to the development of cancers.

QUESTIONS

11 The speed of ultrasound in soft tissue is 1500 m/s. The time delay for an echo from ultrasound in soft tissue was 0.0002 seconds. At what depth was it reflected?

12 The difference in time between the return of ultrasound pulses from either side of the head of a foetus is 140 µs (140×10^{-6} seconds). The standard speed of ultrasound in the head is 1500 m/s. Calculate the size of the foetal head.

A first look...

SELF-CHECK ACTIVITY

CONTEXT

Ben and Louise are sitting in their local hospital waiting room. It is Louise who is to be examined, though she is not injured or unwell. She is pregnant and her doctor has calculated that this is her 16th week of pregnancy. It is routine for pregnant women to have an ultrasound scan at this stage, so she and Ben have taken time off work for the appointment.

They are both excited and a little anxious. This is their first child and they are not quite sure what the procedure is. Louise had three cups of herbal tea shortly before they came to the hospital because she had been told that the scan gives a clearer image if her bladder is full. She has changed to drinking herbal tea because since being pregnant she has gone off the taste of ordinary tea!

A few minutes later they are called into a room that has a bed and some equipment nearby. Mary, the operator, asks Louise to lie on the bed and then she dims the lights. She moves a computer screen into view, lifts Louise's blouse and squirts some clear gel on to Louise's belly. Mary then rests a probe on the gel on Louise's skin to make a good contact. It feels cold but Louise soon forgets this as an image comes into view on the screen.

Louise had imagined that the image of their baby would be rather fuzzy and difficult to understand, especially if you were not used to making sense of medical images. She thought it would have to be explained to her. In fact, she gasped in amazement as a tiny figure appeared. It was easy to see the shape of its body, backbone and even its heart beating. It was active as well, its little arms and legs moving around.

Mary turns the probe to get a cross-sectional view. She then uses a tracker ball to trace round the perimeter of the skull on the image and then zooms in on the spine to take a closer look.

It was hard to believe that this was all being done with sound waves. The probe resting on Louise's tummy was producing a stream of high frequency sound waves, which passed through her body, including her womb and the baby's body. Where there was a difference in density, some of the waves were reflected and the probe picked up the reflections.

All too soon it was over. Mary had the information she needed, the baby was doing well and there were other people waiting. Ben and Louise could have spent much longer gazing at the screen but Mary gave them a printout of one of the images to take away with them. Thankfully the ultrasound scan had not shown anything wrong with the baby and now she or he seemed even more real.

How does an ultrasound machine detect if a wave has been reflected from near the surface or deeper down in the body? Why does it need this information?

Hospitals make extensive use of X-rays. Find out why these are not used to get images of unborn babies.

What does 'difference in density' mean? Look at the diagram of a baby in the womb. Where are the changes in density going to be?

Mary said that the measurement of the circumference of the skull was to check that Louise was 16 weeks pregnant. How did that help?

Ultrasound scans are not done to give parents pictures of babies – that is an added bonus. Mary is a highly trained operator – what features do you think she is looking for in particular?

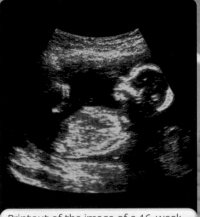

Printout of the image of a 16-week-old foetus during an ultrasound scan.

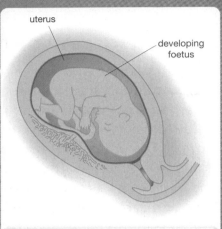

uterus

developing foetus

The foetus in the womb.

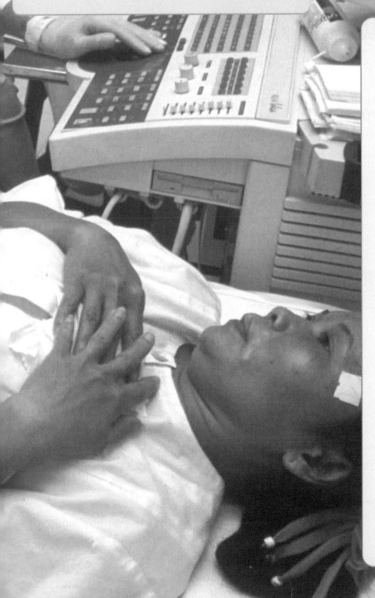

Maximise your grade

These sentences show what you need to be including in your work. Use these to improve your work and to be successful.

Grade	Answer includes...
F	State the reason why ultrasound cannot be heard by humans.
	State an effect on the body of exposure to X-rays.
	Explain why ultrasound is used instead of X-rays to monitor the progress of a baby in the womb.
C	State the relationship between skull circumference and number of weeks since fertilisation.
	Explain what is meant by the term density.
	Describe differences in density of body parts and explain where such changes may occur.
A	Explain how the reflection of ultrasound allows distance to be calculated and hence produce a three dimensional image.
	Explain how information from the ultrasound scan can be used by a trained operator to identify abnormalities in the development of a baby in the womb.

Treatment

You will find out:
- about nuclear radiation
- how nuclear radiation is used in medicine
- about beta and gamma radiation
- about X-rays

Treating cancers

Nuclear radiation and high energy X-rays are used to treat cancers. The photograph shows a patient undergoing gamma knife radiotherapy to treat a brain tumour. The patient receives a dose of gamma radiation. Their head is held in place by a metal frame. Radiation is targeted at a specific area of the brain and has a minimal effect on surrounding areas. It is non-invasive and provides access to areas of the brain that cannot be reached by other techniques.

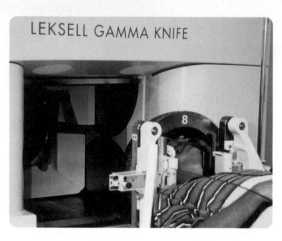

LEKSELL GAMMA KNIFE

Using radiation

Radiation emitted from the **nucleus** of an **atom** is used in medicine for:
- diagnosis (finding out what is wrong)
- therapy (treatment).

Gamma (γ) radiation is usually used for diagnosis and for therapy.

X-rays are also used for diagnosis and for therapy.

X-rays and gamma rays are both **electromagnetic waves** that have very short wavelengths.

They are both very **penetrating** and can pass into the body to treat internal organs.

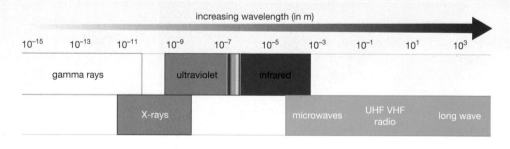

increasing wavelength (in m)

| 10^{-15} | 10^{-13} | 10^{-11} | 10^{-9} | 10^{-7} | 10^{-5} | 10^{-3} | 10^{-1} | 10^{1} | 10^{3} |

gamma rays | ultraviolet | infrared

X-rays | microwaves | UHF VHF radio | long wave

FIGURE 1: The electromagnetic spectrum. Gamma rays and X-rays have a very short wavelength.

- Other electromagnetic waves (such as light and radio waves) do not penetrate the body.
- Other types of nuclear radiation (**alpha** and **beta** particles) do not penetrate inside the body.

Nuclear radiation damages living cells. Exposing living organisms to nuclear radiation should be avoided.

QUESTIONS

1. What is the difference between diagnosis and therapy?
2. What do X-rays and gamma rays have in common?

Watch Out
X-rays are NOT emitted from the nucleus of an atom.

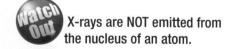

...alpha ...atom ...beta ...cancer ...cobalt-60 ...electromagnetic wave ...film badge

What sort of nuclear radiation is used for therapy?

Radiation emitted from the nucleus of an unstable atom can be alpha (α), beta (β) or gamma (γ).

Radiation	Alpha	Beta	Gamma
Ionising power	very strong	medium	weak
Range in air	about 5 cm	about 1 m	large, its intensity reduces with distance
What stops it?	paper	aluminium	greatly reduced by thick lead

When nuclear radiation passes through a material it causes **ionisation**. Ionising radiation damages living cells, increasing the risk of **cancer**.

Nuclear radiation can be used to kill cells and living organisms. Cancer cells can be destroyed by exposing the affected area of the body to large amounts of radiation. This is called **radiotherapy**.

- Alpha radiation is absorbed by the skin so is of no use for diagnosis or in therapy.
- Beta radiation passes through skin but not bone. Its medical applications are limited but it is used, for example to treat the eyes.
- Gamma radiation is a very penetrating nuclear radiation and is used in medicine. **Cobalt-60** is a gamma-emitting radioactive material that is widely used to treat cancers.

Danger of alpha particles

Alpha particles are damaging if they enter the body. This happens if a source of alpha radiation is swallowed or breathed in. Radon gas decays by emitting alpha particles and is dangerous if it is breathed in.

Radiation protection

A **film badge** is worn by people who work with radioactive substances. It monitors a worker's exposure to radiation. The badge contains a piece of photographic film. Radiation affects the film in a similar way to light. The badge's exterior is of different thicknesses; this allows different areas of the film to be used to measure a worker's exposure to different types of radiation having different penetrating powers.

FIGURE 2: A film badge worn by a person working with radioactive substances. Why are these badges worn?

Gamma radiation

When the nucleus of an atom of a radioactive substance decays it emits an alpha or a beta particle. It loses any surplus energy by emitting gamma rays.

How X-rays are produced

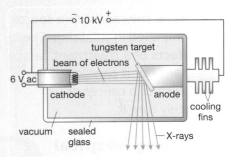

FIGURE 3: An X-ray tube used to produce X-rays.

- A hot cathode emits electrons that are attracted by a highly positive target.
- When the fast-moving electrons hit the target some of their **kinetic energy** is used to emit X-rays but most of it is converted to heat.

Comparing X-rays and gamma rays

- X-rays and gamma rays are exactly the same; they only differ in their origin.
- An X-ray machine allows the rate of production and energy of the X-rays to be controlled, but you cannot change the gamma radiation emitted from a particular radioactive source.
- X-rays can have a much higher energy than gamma rays.

QUESTIONS

3 Alpha radiation is of no use in medicine. Why?
4 Why must exposure to nuclear radiation be avoided?
5 Which type of nuclear radiation is used to treat a cancer deep inside the body?

QUESTIONS

6 Suggest why there is a vacuum in an X-ray tube.
7 Give **one** advantage of using X-rays rather than gamma rays as a source of radiation.

...*gamma* ...*ionisation* ...*kinetic energy* ...*nucleus* ...*penetrating* ...*radiation* ...*radiotherapy* ...*X-ray*

What is radioactivity?

You will find out:

- how to measure the activity of radioactive materials
- about the radiation given out by radioisotopes
- about the half-life of radioisotopes

Marie Curie's achievements

Marie Curie (1867–1934) was a famous Polish scientist who researched radioactivity.

In 1903 she won the Nobel Prize for physics with her husband Pierre for their work on the three types of radiation emitted – alpha, beta and gamma.

In 1911 she won the Nobel Prize again, for chemistry, for the discovery of two new elements, radium and polonium.

She died of leukaemia caused by radiation in 1934. Pierre was killed when he was run over by a cart in Paris in 1906.

Marie Curie measuring the activity of a radioactive material between 1897 and 1899.

Measuring radiation

A Geiger-Müller tube and ratemeter (together called a **Geiger counter**) are used to detect the rate of **decay** of a radioactive substance. Each 'click' sound or number on the display screen represents the decay of one **nucleus**. **Radiation** is emitted when a nucleus decays.

Activity is measured by counting the average number of nuclei that decay every second. This is also called the **count rate**.

Activity is measured in counts per second or **becquerels** (Bq).

$$\text{activity} = \frac{\text{number of nuclei that decay}}{\text{time taken in seconds}} \quad \text{the unit is Bq}$$

The activity of a radioactive substance decreases with time. This is shown by the count rate falling.

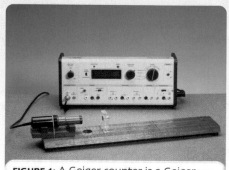

FIGURE 1: A Geiger counter is a Geiger-Müller tube and ratemeter. What does a Geiger counter measure?

QUESTIONS

1   The activity of a radioactive source is 200 Bq. How many counts would be recorded in 10 seconds?

2   Sam records a count of 4000 in 25 seconds from a radioactive source. What is its activity?

...activity ...alpha ...becquerel ...beta ...count rate ...decay

Radioactive decay

Radioactive substances decay naturally and give out **alpha** (α), **beta** (β) and **gamma** (γ) radiation. The Curies and Becquerel identified and named the three different types of radiation.

Radioactive decay is a **random** process. It is not possible to predict when a nucleus will decay. Decay is independent of physical conditions such as temperature.

However, there are so many atoms in even the smallest amount of **radioisotope** that an average count rate can be calculated. Compare this with throwing dice. In a large number of throws, one-sixth of each number will turn up.

Radioisotopes

FIGURE 2: Pitchblende. A radioisotope that is a form of uranium oxide and which emits alpha particles.

A radioisotope has nuclei that are unstable because its nuclear particles are not held together strongly enough. Some particles break free and release an alpha or beta particle. Sometimes gamma rays are emitted to make the nucleus more stable. Gamma radiation is a high frequency electromagnetic wave carrying excess energy away from a nucleus.

The largest stable nucleus is an isotope of lead. This is why lead is often found near radioactive rocks.

▦▦▦ QUESTIONS ▦▦▦

3 What can you say about all the isotopes of the elements above lead in the periodic table?

4 Sita records the count rate from a radioactive source. She takes four readings. They are 138 Bq, 149 Bq, 133 Bq and 142 Bq. Why are the readings different?

Half-life

The rate of radioactive decay:

- is different for different radioisotopes
- depends on the number of nuclei of the radioisotope present; the more nuclei present the greater the rate of decay.

> The **half-life** of a radioisotope is the average time it takes for half the nuclei present to decay.

The half-life of a radioisotope cannot be changed.

example

In an experiment to find the half-life of a radioisotope, the following results are obtained and a graph of activity against time is drawn.

Time in minutes	Activity in Bq
0	100
1	50
2	25
3	13

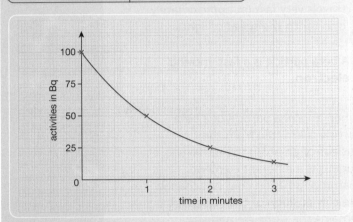

The initial activity is 100 Bq. The average time for the activity to halve from 100 to 50 Bq, 50 to 25 Bq and so on is 1 minute. The half-life is 1 minute.

The half-lives of different radioactive isotopes vary from a fraction of a second to millions of years.

▦▦▦ QUESTIONS ▦▦▦

5 Why is the half-life of a radioisotope an approximate value?

6 The activity of a radioactive sample took 4 hours to decrease from 100 Bq to 25 Bq. What is its half-life?

7 A radioactive substance has a half-life of 2 hours. How much of it remains after 6 hours?

Uses of radioisotopes

You will find out:

- about background radiation
- how background radiation is caused
- how tracers are used

Radon risks

Granite rocks contain small amounts of radioactive uranium. When uranium decays it emits radon gas that is also radioactive.

In granite areas, such as Devon and Cornwall, where houses were traditionally built from granite, there is concern about the health risks to the inhabitants who may be harmed by breathing in radon gas.

Background radiation

Background radiation is ionising radiation that is always present in the environment. It varies from place to place and from day to day. The level of background radiation is low and does not cause harm.

Tracers

Radioisotopes are used as **tracers** in industry, research and medicine.

Tracers are used to:

- detect leaks in underground pipes
- monitor the uptake of fertilisers in plants
- check for a blockage in a patient's blood vessel.

FIGURE 1: Burying an oil pipeline underground. What is used to detect leaks in an underground pipe?

Smoke alarm

One type of **smoke detector** uses a source of **alpha particles** to detect smoke. It is sensitive to low levels of smoke.

FIGURE 2: A smoke alarm is used to detect smoke.

QUESTIONS

1   Suggest how the uptake of a fertiliser in a plant is monitored.
2   Why should all houses have smoke alarms fitted?

...alpha particle   ...americium-241   ...background radiation   ...cosmic ray

Causes of background radiation

Background radiation is caused by:

- radioactive substances present in rocks and soil
- **cosmic rays** from Space.

Uses of tracers

In addition to medical applications, tracers are used to:

- track the dispersal of waste materials
- find leaks or blockages in underground pipes
- track the route of underground pipes.

How a smoke alarm works

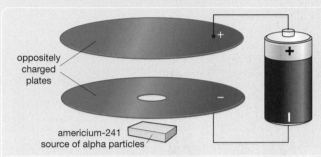

FIGURE 3: The radioisotope americium-241 emits alpha particles inside a smoke alarm. How does the detector work?

Many smoke detectors contain a radioisotope such as **americium-241** that emits alpha particles.

- The alpha particles ionise some of the oxygen and nitrogen atoms in the air.
- The positive ions and negative electrons move towards the negative and positive plates respectively.
- This creates a tiny current that is detected by electronic circuitry in the smoke alarm.
- If smoke particles enter they attach themselves to the ions, neutralising them.
- The smoke detector senses the drop in current and sets off an alarm.

Americium-241 has a long **half-life** of about 28 years. This is important as:

- the source does not need to be replaced frequently
- a decrease in ionisation current is due to the presence of smoke and not the decay of the source reducing the number of ions present.

More on background radiation

Most background radiation is from natural sources such as rocks and cosmic rays.

Human activity contributes less than 1 per cent to the level of background radiation. Examples are:

- waste products from nuclear power stations and other industries
- waste products from hospitals
- man-made radioisotopes obtained by firing particles such as neutrons at stable nuclei, making them unstable and causing them to decay.

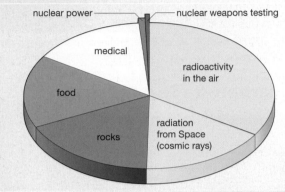

FIGURE 4: Sources of background radiation. Which is the largest source?

How are tracers used in industry?

To locate a leak or blockage in an underground gas pipe using a tracer:

- a very small amount of a suitable radioisotope that emits **gamma radiation** is put into the pipe
- a detector is passed along the ground above the path of the pipe
- an increase in activity is detected in the region of the leak or blockage and little or no activity is detected after this point.

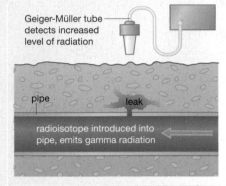

FIGURE 5: Using a gamma-emitting radioisotope to detect a leak in a pipe. Why does the reading on the Geiger-Müller tube fall rapidly after the leak has been passed over?

Dating rocks

Some rock types such as granite contain traces of **uranium**. All uranium isotopes are radioactive. These uranium isotopes go through a series of decays, eventually forming a stable isotope of **lead**.

By comparing the amounts of uranium and lead present in a rock sample, its approximate age can be found.

FIGURE 6: Granite rocks. How can the approximate age of these rocks be found?

Radiocarbon-dating

FIGURE 7: The Turin shroud was originally thought to have been worn by Jesus Christ. However, recent radiocarbon-dating has suggested the shroud is only about 500 years old, which is long after the time of Christ.

FIGURE 8: A section of The Scroll of Isaiah, one of the Dead Sea Scrolls.

Carbon-14 is a radioactive isotope of carbon. Carbon is present in all living things. By measuring the amount of carbon-14 present in an archaeological find, its approximate age can be found.

In 1947 a shepherd discovered the Dead Sea Scrolls in caves at Qumran in Jordan. Radiocarbon-dating was used to estimate their age. They were found to be about 2000 years old and are likely to be genuine.

QUESTIONS

7   Which of the following could **not** be dated using carbon-14?

   wool jumper   wooden axe   iron nail   nylon shirt   cotton sheet

8   Why is lead always found with radioactive rocks?

...carbon-14 ...lead ...ratio

Dating rocks and the radioactive series

Use of uranium-238

Uranium-238 decays, with a very long half-life of 4500 million years, to form thorium which is also **unstable**.

$$^{238}_{92}\text{U} \longrightarrow {}^{234}_{90}\text{Th}\ (+\ {}^{4}_{2}\text{He}) \longrightarrow {}^{234}_{91}\text{Pa}\ (+\ {}^{0}_{-1}\text{e}) \longrightarrow \text{------------} \longrightarrow {}^{206}_{82}\text{Pb}$$

A series of unstable isotopes is formed, all with relatively short half-lives, until a stable isotope, lead-206, is formed. (Lead is the element with the highest atomic number that has stable isotopes.)

The **ratio** of uranium to lead in a sample of rock indicates the age of the rock. The proportion of lead increases as time increases. If there are equal quantities of $^{238}_{92}\text{U}$ and $^{206}_{82}\text{Pb}$, the rock is 4500 million years (one half-life) old.

Use of uranium-235

Uranium-235 has a shorter half-life than that of uranium-238 of approximately 700 million years and it is used to date younger rocks.

More on radiocarbon-dating

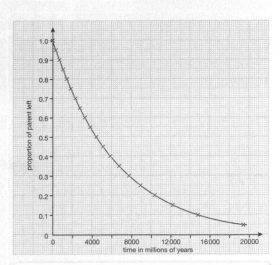

FIGURE 9: Radioactive decay of uranium-238. What stable isotope does it form?

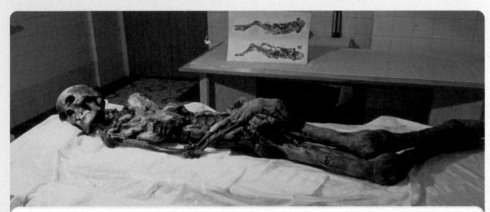

FIGURE 11: The preserved remains of 'Ice Maiden', a young woman found in 1993 in ice in central Asia. The body has been dated to approximately 2500 years old. She is so well preserved that tattoos can still be seen on her skin.

FIGURE 10: Uranium-235 was used to date this rock sample brought back from the Moon by an Apollo mission. It was formed from solidified lava. The Moon rocks, and hence the Moon, were found to be about 4400 million years old.

- Cosmic rays enter Earth's atmosphere and collide with atoms that release neutrons from their nuclei. The energetic neutrons collide with nitrogen atoms forming carbon-14. The amount of carbon-14 in the atmosphere has not changed for thousands of years.

- Only a very small fraction of the carbon present in living things is carbon-14 (about 1 in 10^{12} atoms). (It is mainly stable carbon-12.)

- Plants absorb carbon dioxide in photosynthesis. Animals and humans eat plants and take in carbon-14.

- When a living thing such as a tree or an animal dies it stops exchanging carbon with the atmosphere.

- The carbon-14 present decays to nitrogen with a half-life of about 5700 years.

$$^{14}_{6}\text{C} \longrightarrow {}^{14}_{7}\text{N}\ (+\ {}^{0}_{-1}\text{e})$$

- By looking at the ratio of carbon-12 to carbon-14 in a sample from the dead organism and comparing it to the ratio in a living organism, the age of a dead organism can be estimated quite accurately.

- Carbon-14 decays very slowly so the method is not suitable for dating organisms that are a few hundred years old.

QUESTIONS

9 The ratio of $^{238}_{92}\text{U}$ to $^{206}_{82}\text{Pb}$ in a rock sample is 1 : 4.

 a How old is the rock?

 b Why does this suggest the rock did not originate on Earth?

10 Why is carbon-14 dating not suitable for finding the age of a *very* old skeleton?

Fission

You will find out:

- how nuclear power stations use uranium as a fuel
- how electricity is generated in power stations
- how uranium releases energy

Fission – friend or foe?

Fission is the splitting of a large nucleus such as uranium to release energy. Fission was used with devastating effects in the atom bombs that were dropped on each of the cities of Hiroshima and Nagasaki in 1945.

These days, controlled fission is used in nuclear power stations to produce electricity.

An atom bomb explosion.

DID YOU KNOW?

Only 1 kg of uranium-235 produces about the same amount of energy as 2 million kg of coal!

Power stations

A **power station** makes **electricity**. It uses an energy source such as coal, oil, gas or nuclear to:

- heat water
- produce steam
- turn a **turbine**
- generate electricity.

Power stations that use **renewable energy** sources such as wind and water do not use steam to turn the turbine. For example, in a hydroelectric power station the kinetic energy of falling water is used to turn a turbine.

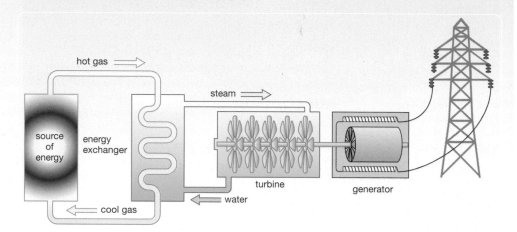

FIGURE 1: The stages of producing electricity in a power station. What types of fuels can power stations use?

A **nuclear** power station uses **uranium** as a fuel instead of burning coal, oil or gas to heat the water.

The **fission** of uranium can set up a **chain reaction** that produces a large amount of energy.

FIGURE 2: A nuclear power station. What do nuclear power stations use as a fuel?

QUESTIONS

1. What happens to the uranium fuel in a nuclear power station?
2. What is the difference between a coal-fired and a nuclear power station?

...chain reaction   ...electricity   ...fission   ...neutron   ...nuclear   ...nucleus

How a nuclear power station works

Natural uranium consists of two isotopes, uranium-235 and uranium-238.

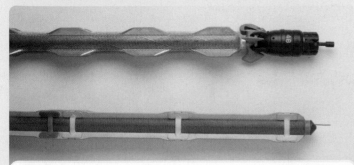

FIGURE 3: Fuel rods in a nuclear power station. What material are they made from?

The fuel used in a nuclear power station contains a greater proportion of the uranium-235 isotope than occurs naturally. The fuel is called 'enriched uranium' and forms the fuel rods.

Fission occurs when a large unstable **nucleus** is split up and there is a release of energy in the form of heat.

- The fission of uranium in a nuclear reactor produces heat.
- The heat is used to boil water to produce steam.
- The pressure of the steam acts on the turbine blades which turn.
- The rotating turbine turns the generator that produces electricity.

FIGURE 4: Turbine and generator in a nuclear power station. What is the function of each?

QUESTIONS

3. What is 'enriched uranium'?
4. How is heat produced in a nuclear power station?
5. In a nuclear power station, what makes the turbine blades turn?

How does uranium release energy?

In a nuclear power station, atoms of uranium-235 are bombarded with **neutrons**.

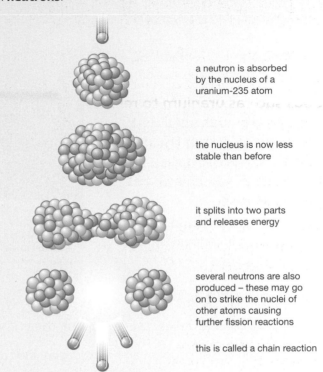

a neutron is absorbed by the nucleus of a uranium-235 atom

the nucleus is now less stable than before

it splits into two parts and releases energy

several neutrons are also produced – these may go on to strike the nuclei of other atoms causing further fission reactions

this is called a chain reaction

FIGURE 5: Uranium-235 undergoes a chain reaction that produces a large amount of energy.

The decay of uranium-235 can be shown as:

$$^{235}_{92}U + ^1_0n \longrightarrow ^{90}_{36}Kr + ^{143}_{56}Ba + 3(^1_0n) + \gamma \text{ rays}$$

The extra neutrons emitted cause a chain reaction and produce a large amount of energy.

Uranium-235 nuclei do not always split in the same way but extra neutrons are always emitted.

Uses of nuclear fuel

- An atomic bomb. If the uranium is above a certain critical size (about the size of a tennis ball) fission occurs spontaneously.
- A nuclear submarine is powered by a nuclear **reactor** in a similar way to a nuclear power station.

QUESTIONS

6. In what way is fission:
   a. similar to radioactive decay?
   b. different to radioactive decay?
7. The fission of a uranium-235 nucleus releases three neutrons that initiate a chain reaction. How many uranium nuclei can be split after four more stages of the chain reaction?

Chain reaction

A chain reaction can carry on for as long as any of the uranium fuel remains. This allows large amounts of energy to be produced.

- An atomic bomb is a chain reaction that has gone out of control. The chain reaction produces huge amounts of energy. The atomic bomb causes devastation equivalent to many 'ordinary' bombs and health risks resulting from exposure to nuclear radiation.

- In a nuclear power station the chain reaction is controlled to produce a steady supply of heat.

You will find out:

- how materials can become radioactive
- about problems of radioactive wastes
- how scientists stop nuclear reactions going out of control

FIGURE 6: The city of Hiroshima after the atomic bomb was dropped on it. The nuclear radiation effects are still causing the inhabitants to develop cancers.

Artificial radioactivity

Materials can be made radioactive by putting them into a nuclear reactor.

Such man-made radioisotopes can be produced with different properties that make them ideal for different uses in:

- hospitals to diagnose and treat patients
- industry as tracers to detect leaks.

FIGURE 7: Tops of uranium rods in a nuclear reactor. What advantages do man-made radioisotopes produced in it have?

QUESTIONS

8 Why are people still affected by the atomic bomb dropped on Hiroshima in 1945?

9 How can materials be made radioactive?

10 What is meant by the term 'chain reaction'?

...control rod   ...moderator

Radioactive waste

Nuclear fission produces **radioactive waste**. This is a major problem since the waste products have to be handled carefully and disposed of safely.

- Very low-level waste such as that produced by medical applications is placed in sealed plastic bags then buried or incinerated (burned) under strict controls. Other low-level waste may be embedded in glass discs and buried in the sea.

FIGURE 8: Transporting flasks of nuclear waste by train across the UK to the Sellafield reprocessing plant. Can you suggest why some people are concerned about the way in which radioactive waste is transported and the health risks to those people living near to Sellafield?

- High-level waste such as spent fuel rods can be **reprocessed** to make radioactive materials for reuse.

Sellafield in Cumbria is a reprocessing plant that takes radioactive waste from all over the world. Sellafield has been described as 'a nuclear dustbin for the world'.

Artificial radioactivity

Useful radioisotopes are produced by bombarding atoms with neutrons present in a nuclear reactor. Neutrons are uncharged so they are easily captured by many nuclei, producing unstable isotopes.

For example, when magnesium sulphate is irradiated with neutrons in a reactor it produces radioactive magnesium-28. A tiny amount of this radioisotope is added to a liquid fertiliser and plants are watered with it. Its passage through the plant is traced to monitor the movement of the fertiliser in the plant.

QUESTIONS

11 The radioisotope cobalt-60, used to treat cancers, is made by firing neutrons at cobalt-59.
   a What happens to:
      i the atomic number of the cobalt nucleus?
      ii the mass number of the cobalt nucleus?
   b What type of radiation is emitted?
12 Suggest **two** problems associated with nuclear power stations.

Controlling nuclear fission

The design of a nuclear reactor includes measures to control the number of fission reactions so that the amount of energy released can be controlled.

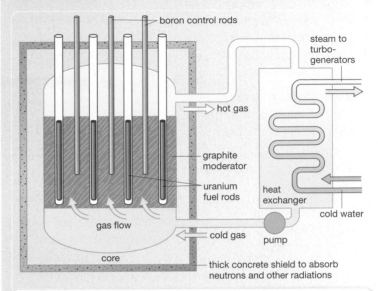

FIGURE 9: A gas-cooled nuclear reactor. Why is it important to be able to control the number of fission reactions in a reactor?

The output of a nuclear reactor is controlled by:

- a graphite **moderator** between the fuel rods that slows down fast-moving neutrons emitted during fission. Slow-moving neutrons are more likely to be captured by other uranium nuclei, which maintains the chain reaction
- boron **control rods** between the fuel rods. Boron absorbs neutrons so fewer neutrons are available to split more uranium nuclei. The boron rods can be raised or lowered in the reactor, which controls the fission rate.

Decommissioning

A nuclear power station cannot be demolished nor the site developed for other purposes. The reactor building is embedded in thick concrete and left for approximately 150 years until radiation levels have fallen to a safe value.

Sellafield has been described as 'a nuclear dustbin for the world'.

QUESTIONS

13 The boron control rods in a reactor are raised. Explain how this affects the energy produced.
14 What is the purpose of a moderator in a nuclear reactor?

Module summary

Concept map

There are two kinds of electric charge, positive and negative.

Like charges repel, unlike charges attract.

Electrostatics

Electrostatic effects are caused by the transfer of electrons.

A positively charged object lacks electrons. A negatively charged object has an excess of electrons.

You can get an electric shock if you become charged then earthed.

Some uses of electrostatics are:

- defibrillators
- paint sprayers
- photocopiers
- dust precipitators.

An electric current is a flow of electric charge.

Using electricity safely

The fuse is connected in the live side. It melts if the current exceeds its stated value, breaking the circuit.

Electric circuits need a complete loop to work. Resistors are used to change the current in a circuit.

Ultrasound scans allow a doctor to see inside you without surgery. It can be used to measure the rate of blood flow in the body and to break up kidney or gall stones.

Ultrasound is sound of a higher frequency than we can hear (above 20 000 Hz).

Sound is a longitudinal wave; the particles vibrate in the same direction as the wave travels.

- Wavelength (γ) is the distance occupied by one complete wave.
- Frequency (f) is the number of complete waves in 1 second.
- Amplitude is the maximum distance a particle moves from its normal position.

Medical uses of radioactivity

- For diagnosis, as a tracer.
- To sterilise equipment.
- To treat cancers.

Nuclear radiation is emitted from the nuclei of radioactive materials:

- alpha particle – helium nucleus
- beta particle – fast-moving electron
- gamma radiation – electromagnetic waves

Half-life of a radioisotope is the average time for half the nuclei present to decay.

Gamma radiation, widely used for medical purposes, is the most penetrating.

Fission is the splitting of a large nucleus, such as uranium, releasing energy. This can set up a chain reaction producing a large amount of energy, as in a nuclear power station or atomic bomb.

X-rays are similar to gamma rays but are produced by firing high-speed electrons at a metal target.

Module quiz

1 What charge does a polythene rod acquire when it is rubbed with a duster?

2 What happens if two negatively charged balloons are brought near each other?

3 Why are the tanks on oil tankers often filled with nitrogen before they are cleaned?

4 Why do paint sprayers charge the paint droplets?

5 What does a dust precipitator do?

6 A resistor has a potential difference of 12 V across it when the current in it is 0.5 A. What is its resistance?

7 What colours are the live, neutral and earth wires in a cable used to connect an electric kettle to its plug?

8 What is ultrasound?

9 Give **two** practical applications of ultrasound.

10 Give **one** similarity and **one** difference between X-rays and gamma rays.

11 What is meant by the term 'radioisotope'?

12 What type of radiation is emitted by a radioactive tracer?

13 What is the difference between therapy and diagnosis?

14 How many counts would be recorded in 30 seconds if the activity of a radioactive source is 200 Bq?

15 Why would your answer to question **14** only be an approximate value?

16 Which type of nuclear radiation is stopped by a few millimetres of aluminium?

17 What is meant by 'background radiation'?

18 What radioisotope would be used to estimate the age of a bone found in an archaeological dig?

19 What is meant by 'nuclear fission'?

20 What is a 'chain reaction'?

Data analysis activity

The table shows the properties of some radioisotopes.

QUESTIONS 1 Decide which isotope you would use in each of the following cases:

    a in a smoke detector

    b to check for a blockage in an air passage in a patient's lungs

    c to treat a brain tumour

    d to control the thickness of paper in a rolling mill

    e as a tracer to detect a tumour in a patient's liver.

Isotope	State	Type of radiation	Half-life
cobalt-60	solid	gamma	5 years
technetium-99m	liquid	gamma	6 hours
americium-241	solid	alpha	433 years
strontium-90	solid	beta	28 years
xenon-133	gas	gamma	5 days

Introduction

One-third of the marks towards your GCSE Additional Science examination comes from work that is marked by your teachers. This allows you to build up your marks whilst you are still following the course. The work is designed to motivate you and give you a sense of achievement.

There are three types of work:

- practical skills
- research study
- data task.

Practical skills

Your teacher will award you a maximum of six marks for being able to **work safely and accurately when carrying out practical activities in science**.

- If you can work safely and accurately with a lot of support and guidance, you may be awarded one or two marks.

- If you need no help and are fully aware of the risks in performing experiments, you may be awarded all six marks.

RESEARCH STUDY

Scientific ideas and discoveries affect our everyday lives in many different ways. Over a period of time, ideas develop and actually change the way we think and the way we view the world around us. Scientific discoveries have influenced technological advances in fields as diverse as medicine and meteorology, astronomy and geology.

You will be given a research study that contains some stimulus material and a number of tasks to perform based on the stimulus material. These tasks will be graded in difficulty, starting with the more straightforward and finishing with an open-ended task allowing you to show your research skills to the full.

Over the following week you will have to find out as much as you can about the research topic. This will mean reading books, looking at CD-ROMs and searching the Internet.

You may need to photocopy pictures or articles to help you complete the tasks.

When the week is up, you will have time during lessons to write your report. What is important is how you have collected and interpreted information.

- You will need to show an understanding of how scientific ideas have changed over a period of time and discuss some of the social, economic and environmental effects.

- Your report must be between 400 and 800 words. Anything longer means you have not been selective.

- Try to include pictures, graphs or diagrams to illustrate the important points in your report.

- Remember to list all the sources of information you have used. If you quote from an article, book or website, you must include the source of the information.

- Your work can be handwritten or word processed and your ability to use correct scientific and technical language, as well as your spelling, punctuation and grammar will be looked at.

Your best report, the one that scores the most marks out of 24, will be the one that counts towards your GCSE.

HOW ARE MARKS AWARDED?

The research study   The use of nuclear power in the UK

The stimulus material   • Photographs of a nuclear power station.

• Relevant statement.

> Nearly 200 000 sheep in North Wales are still
> under restrictions imposed following the
> Chernobyl disaster of 1986.

• Series of questions, of increasing demand, to guide
  your research.

> 1 What happened at Chernobyl in 1986?
> 2 When was the first nuclear power station opened in
>   the UK? When did it stop generating electricity?
> 3 Use an outline map of the UK to plot the locations
>   of nuclear power stations. Suggest reasons for
>   their locations.
> 4 How have the amounts of electricity generated by
>   nuclear power stations changed since the first
>   nuclear power station was opened?
> 5 The public's view on nuclear power has changed over
>   the past 50 years. What effect has this had on the
>   building of nuclear power stations? What other
>   factors have affected the use of nuclear power
>   stations in generating electricity?

Four areas of report writing will be marked. Each area can score up to six marks.

You will not be allowed to redraft your report. During the course, you may be given two or three opportunities to write a report like this. The idea is that you learn from the feedback you are given each time.

What information have you collected?

■ Look at the stimulus material you have been given.

■ What else do you need to find out to be able to answer the questions?

■ Look at a variety of sources, both printed and electronic. Make a list of the sources you use.

How has the information you have found helped you to understand scientific ideas?

■ You need to show clearly that you understand how ideas about the topic have changed over a period of time.

■ You also need to explain how those ideas have affected technology and how they are linked to social, economic and environmental issues.

How does the information you have found help you to understand the research topic?

■ You need to make a link between the information you have found and the topic. Once you have made the link, use the information to answer the questions.

■ It is important that you show how ideas about the topic have changed over a period of time.

How well have you presented the information you have found?

■ You need to provide answers that are clear enough for other people to understand. Your writing should be accurate, using scientific and technical terms correctly.

It is important that you are able to analyse and evaluate data.

During the course, you will have several opportunities to collect data then analyse and evaluate what you have collected.

You will not be assessed on your collection of data; indeed, your teacher may collect the data for you or provide you with sample data. Data can also be collected from computer simulations of experiments.

You will write a report based on questions that have been given to you. Your work can be handwritten or word processed.

Five areas of report writing will be marked. Each area can score up to six marks.

Your best report, the one that scores the most marks out of 30, will be the one that counts towards your GCSE.

HOW ARE MARKS AWARDED?

The data task Stopping distances

Student information sheet

You will be given a student information sheet.

It will contain some background information about the task.

> Steep hills sometimes have escape lanes for cars to use in an emergency. If the brakes on a car fail, the car uses the escape lane to slow down and stop safely.

The **task you have to do** is given in the form of a question.

> Is there a link between the steepness of a hill and the distance it takes to stop at the bottom?

There will be a suggested way to collect the data including a possible results table. You may collect the data on your own, working in a group or as a whole class. A computer simulation can be used or you can use the data provided.

Set up the equipment as shown.

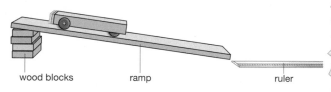

wood blocks   ramp   ruler

Decide on the range of angles to use. The larger the better.

Release the car from the same height each time and measure how far along the ground it goes. Take at least three readings for each angle to ensure you can rely on your measurements.

Record your results in a table like this.

Angle of ramp in °	Distance travelled in cm			
	1st attempt	2nd attempt	3rd attempt	
10				
20				
etc.				

The rest of the task involves **using your data** and must be completed on your own in class.

You will be given a series of questions to answer and will be awarded up to six marks for each answer.

1 Work out the average distance travelled and put the results in your table. Draw a graph of distance travelled against angle. Make sure you choose suitable scales and label the axes. Finish the graph by drawing a suitable line through the points.

If you have a few results plotted and have help with labelling axes, you may be awarded two marks. Four marks may be awarded if results are displayed in appropriate tables and most points are plotted correctly on a suitable graph. For six marks, you will need to have drawn a line of best fit through accurately plotted points.

2 Describe a pattern in your results.

If one trend or pattern has been outlined, you may be awarded two marks. Remember, a trend or pattern should be stated as an '**...er ...er**' statement. For example, 'The steep**er** the slope the great**er** the stopping distance.' Four marks may be awarded if you have processed the data and described the main trends or patterns. For six marks, you will need to process the data to find additional information (for example, the gravitational potential energy at the start) and report any anomalies in your results.

3 How good is the data you used? Is it reliable? Are there any unexpected results? Could the results be improved?

If you make a reasonable attempt to consider the quality of the data or comment on the method used to obtain it, you may be awarded two marks. Four marks may be awarded if you consider the validity and reliability of the data collected. For six marks, you need to give detailed consideration to both the validity and reliability of the data and show an understanding of the limitations of the experimental technique used.

4 Use your scientific knowledge about energy changes to explain your results.

If your conclusion is directly related to the data you have collected, you may be awarded two marks. Four marks may be awarded if the analysis of the data is related to the scientific principles involved. For six marks, you need to give a well-argued justification of your conclusion based on the scientific principles involved.

5 A car's brakes may fail at any point on the hill. Can you work out a way of finding out if the distance the car has to travel down the hill makes any difference to its stopping distance?

If you have made a suitable suggestion for further work you may be awarded two marks. Four marks may be awarded if you have given detailed plans for further experimental work. You will not be expected to do this further work. For six marks, you need to show a clear appreciation of how this further work would lead you to a greater understanding of the topic.

Physical quantities and units

Fundamental physical quantities	
physical quantity	unit(s)
length	metre (m); kilometre (km); centimetre (cm); millimetre (mm)
mass	kilogram (kg); gram (g); milligram (mg)
time	second (s); millisecond (ms); hour (h)
temperature	degree Celsius (°C); kelvin (K)
current	ampere (A); milliampere (mA)
voltage	volt (V); millivolt (mV)

Derived physical quantities	
physical quantity	unit(s)
area	m^2; cm^2; mm^2
volume	m^3; cm^3; mm^3; litre (l); millilitre (ml)
density	kg/m^3; g/cm^3
force	newton (N)
speed	m/s; cm/s; km/h
acceleration	m/s^2; cm/s^2
energy	joule (J); kilojoule (kJ); megajoule (MJ); kilowatt-hour (kWh)
power	watt (W); kilowatt (kW); megawatt (MW)
frequency	hertz (Hz); kilohertz (kHz); megahertz (MHz)
gravitational field strength	N/kg
radioactivity	becquerel (Bq)
specific heat capacity	J/kg°C; J/kgK
specific latent heat	J/kg

Equations used in Additional Science

$$\text{speed} = \frac{\text{distance}}{\text{time}}$$

$$\text{acceleration} = \frac{\text{change in speed}}{\text{time taken}}$$

$$\text{force} = \text{mass} \times \text{acceleration}$$

$$\text{work done} = \text{force} \times \text{distance}$$

$$\text{power} = \frac{\text{work done}}{\text{time}}$$

$$\text{weight} = \text{mass} \times \text{gravitational field strength}$$

$$\text{kinetic energy} = \tfrac{1}{2}mv^2$$

$$\text{potential energy} = mgh$$

$$\text{resistance} = \frac{\text{voltage}}{\text{current}}$$

The maths you need

While studying this course, you will find lots of opportunities to use Mathematics. The maths skills you need are listed below.

Items in the left hand list may be examined in written exam papers covering both Foundation and Higher Tiers. Items in the right hand list may be examined in written exam papers covering the Higher Tier only. You may want to copy the lists and tick off each item when you are satisfied that you can do it.

Both Tiers

I can...

- add, subtract, multiply and divide whole numbers
- recognise and use expressions in decimal form
- make approximations and estimates to obtain reasonable answers
- use simple formulae expressed in words
- understand and use averages
- read, interpret and draw simple inferences from tables and statistical diagrams
- find fractions or percentages of quantities
- construct and interpret pie charts
- calculate with fractions, decimals, percentage or ratio
- solve simple equations
- substitute numbers in simple equations
- interpret and use graphs
- plot graphs from data provided, given the axes and scales
- choose, by simple inspection, and then draw the best smooth curve through a set of points on a graph

Higher Tier only

I can...

- recognise and use expressions in standard form
- manipulate equations
- select appropriate axes and scales for graph plotting
- determine the intercept of a linear graph
- understand and use inverse proportion
- calculate the gradient of a graph
- use statistical methods, for example cumulative frequency, box plots and histograms

Periodic table

Key

| relative atomic mass |
| **atomic symbol** |
| name |
| atomic (proton) number |

Example:
| 1 |
| **H** |
| hydrogen |
| 1 |

Group 1	Group 2		Group 3	Group 4	Group 5	Group 6	Group 7	Group 8
								4 **He** helium 2
7 **Li** lithium 3	9 **Be** beryllium 4		11 **B** boron 5	12 **C** carbon 6	14 **N** nitrogen 7	16 **O** oxygen 8	19 **F** fluorine 9	20 **Ne** neon 10
23 **Na** sodium 11	24 **Mg** magnesium 12		27 **Al** aluminium 13	28 **Si** silicon 14	31 **P** phosphorus 15	32 **S** sulfur 16	35.5 **Cl** chlorine 17	40 **Ar** argon 18

Transition metals:

39 **K** potassium 19	40 **Ca** calcium 20	45 **Sc** scandium 21	48 **Ti** titanium 22	51 **V** vanadium 23	52 **Cr** chromium 24	55 **Mn** manganese 25	56 **Fe** iron 26	59 **Co** cobalt 27	59 **Ni** nickel 28	63.5 **Cu** copper 29	65 **Zn** zinc 30	70 **Ga** gallium 31	73 **Ge** germanium 32	75 **As** arsenic 33	79 **Se** selenium 34	80 **Br** bromine 35	84 **Kr** krypton 36
85 **Rb** rubidium 37	88 **Sr** strontium 38	89 **Y** yttrium 39	91 **Zr** zirconium 40	93 **Nb** niobium 41	96 **Mo** molybdenum 42	[98] **Tc** technetium 43	101 **Ru** ruthenium 44	103 **Rh** rhodium 45	106 **Pd** palladium 46	108 **Ag** silver 47	112 **Cd** cadmium 48	115 **In** indium 49	119 **Sn** tin 50	122 **Sb** antimony 51	128 **Te** tellurium 52	127 **I** iodine 53	131 **Xe** xenon 54
133 **Cs** caesium 55	137 **Ba** barium 56	139 **La*** lanthanum 57	178 **Hf** hafnium 72	181 **Ta** tantalum 73	184 **W** tungsten 74	186 **Re** rhenium 75	190 **Os** osmium 76	192 **Ir** iridium 77	195 **Pt** platinum 78	197 **Au** gold 79	201 **Hg** mercury 80	204 **Tl** thallium 81	207 **Pb** lead 82	209 **Bi** bismuth 83	[209] **Po** polonium 84	[210] **At** astatine 85	[222] **Rn** radon 86
[223] **Fr** francium 87	[226] **Ra** radium 88	[227] **Ac*** actinium 89	[261] **Rf** rutherfordium 104	[262] **Db** dubnium 105	[266] **Sg** seaborgium 106	[264] **Bh** bohrium 107	[277] **Hs** hassium 108	[268] **Mt** meitnerium 109	[271] **Ds** darmstadtium 110	[272] **Rg** roentgenium 111

Elements with atomic numbers 112–116 have been reported but not fully authenticated.

* The Lanthanides (atomic numbers 58–71) and the Actinides (atomic numbers 90–103) have been omitted.

Cu and Cl have not been rounded to the nearest whole number.

ABS	anti-lock braking system, which helps cars to stop safely	198
accelerate	to increase the velocity of an object	182, 200
acceleration	the change of velocity in a given time, it is usually measured in metres per second per second (m/s^2)	179, 197
acid	a chemical that turns litmus paper red – it can often dissolve things that water cannot	134, 153
acidic	something with a pH below 7	134
acrosome	a bubble of enzymes at the front of a sperm	29
active site	the part of the molecule where the reaction occurs – used particularly with reference to enzymes	17
active transport	in active transport, cells use energy to transport substances through cell membranes against a concentration gradient	69
aerobic	aerobic respiration breaks down glucose using oxygen to make energy available for chemical reactions in cells	81
air resistance	the force air exerts on an object moving through it; air resistance slows down movement and increases as the moving object gets faster	200, 205
alkali	a substance which makes a solution that turns red litmus paper blue	107, 134
alkali metal	a metal which burns to form a strongly alkaline oxide, e.g. potassium, sodium	106, 112
allotrope	allotropes are different forms of the same element made when the atoms of the element join together in different patterns, e.g. diamond and graphite are allotropes of carbon	161
alpha	the first letter of the Greek alphabet	232, 237
alpha particle	a positively charged particle made of two protons and two neutrons	240
alveoli	the sac-like end of an airway in the lungs; the surface is enlarged to maximise gas exchange	19
ammeter	a meter that measures the current in a wire, in amps	223
ammonia	an alkaline gas with the formula NH_3; it dissolves readily in water to make ammonium hydroxide solution	87, 146
ampere	the unit used to measure electrical current, often abbreviated to amp	223
amplitude	the difference between the highest and lowest points on a wave	226
anaerobic respiration	a series of chemical reactions that transfer energy from glucose into life processes without using oxygen; carbon dioxide and ethanol, or lactic acid, are the end products	75
anion	a negatively-charged ion; it will move towards the anode in an electrolytic cell	116
anode	the positive electrode in a circuit or battery	116
artery	a blood vessel carrying blood away from the heart under high pressure	22
artificial insemination	putting sperm from a male into a female without sex, usually used for breeding cattle	45
aseptic technique	a technique used in microbiological work to prevent infection or contamination of cultures	47
asexual reproduction	reproduction involving just one parent, the offspring are genetically identical to the parent	44
atom	the smallest part of an element, atoms consist of negatively-charged electrons flying around a positively-charged nucleus	98, 102, 215, 232
atomic number	the number of protons in the nucleus of an atom	94
atrium	a thin-walled chamber in the heart, above the ventricle	25
auxin	a chemical produced by the growing tips of plants that promotes cell growth and elongation	37
background radiation	radiation from space and rocks; it is around us all the time and is at a very low level	240

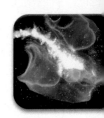

characteristic	characteristics are things that are true about something, e.g. it is a characteristic of mammals that they have fur	40
charge	a property of matter, charge exists in two forms (negative and positive) which attract each other	218, 223
chemical property	the characteristic reactions of a substance	104
chlorination	adding chlorine to a molecule or substance	165
chlorophyll	a green chemical found in photosynthetic plants that allows them to use energy from sunlight to make sugar from carbon dioxide and water	55
chloroplast	a cell structure found in green plants that contains chlorophyll	32, 54

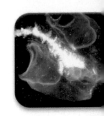

cholesterol	a chemical found particularly in animal fats and foods made from them; the body uses cholesterol to make nerve tissue and some hormones but high levels of cholesterol may make heart attacks more likely	24
chromatography	the science of producing chromatograms, chromatography can use paper or jelly-like films for the soluble substances to move along	159
chromosome	a thread-like body made of DNA and protein found in the nucleus, it only becomes visible during cell division	14

circuit	the complete path around an electrical circuit that electricity can flow along	222
circuit-breaker	a device which breaks a circuit to switch off the power when a danger is detected, it behaves similarly to a fuse	225
clone	two living things are clones if they have exactly the same genes	44
compost	organic material, typically kitchen and garden waste, being rotted down to make fertiliser for the soil	80

compound	a group of atoms bound together, in fixed proportions, by chemical bonds; compounds have different chemical and physical properties to the elements that they contain	96, 121
compression	to push something together, to squeeze it and make it smaller	226
concentration	the amount of material in a given volume	19
concentration gradient	the difference in concentration of a substance between two areas divided by the distance between them	69
conductor	a substance that will let heat or electricity pass through it, e.g. copper	124, 214
consumer	organisms in an ecosystem that use up organic matter produced by other organisms, all animals are consumers	72

continuous process	a process which can continue indefinitely if new materials are added and wastes removed	156
control rod	metal rods which are lowered into nuclear reactors to control the rate of decay and so the temperature of the core	247
coronary artery	the artery that supplies blood to the muscles of the heart	25
corrode	metals react with the air to form powder or crystals and weaken the metal, the word rust is used when iron corrodes	136

cosmic ray	radiation from space that hits the atmosphere, some passes through while some is blocked	241
count rate	the number of nuclear events in a given time, often measured by a Geiger counter	236
covalent bond	a link between two atoms where electrons move around both atoms in the pair; covalent bonds tend to be strong bonds and form between non-metals	161
cracking	the breaking of large organic molecules into smaller ones using heat, pressure and sometimes catalysts	146
crenation	when red blood cells shrink in concentrated solutions, they look partly deflated with a scalloped edge	61

critical temperature	the temperature at which a key event takes place, perhaps a reaction starts or an animal dies	127
crop yield	the mass of useful material produced by a crop	143
cross-breed	to produce an organism by mating individuals from different breeds, varieties, or species	41

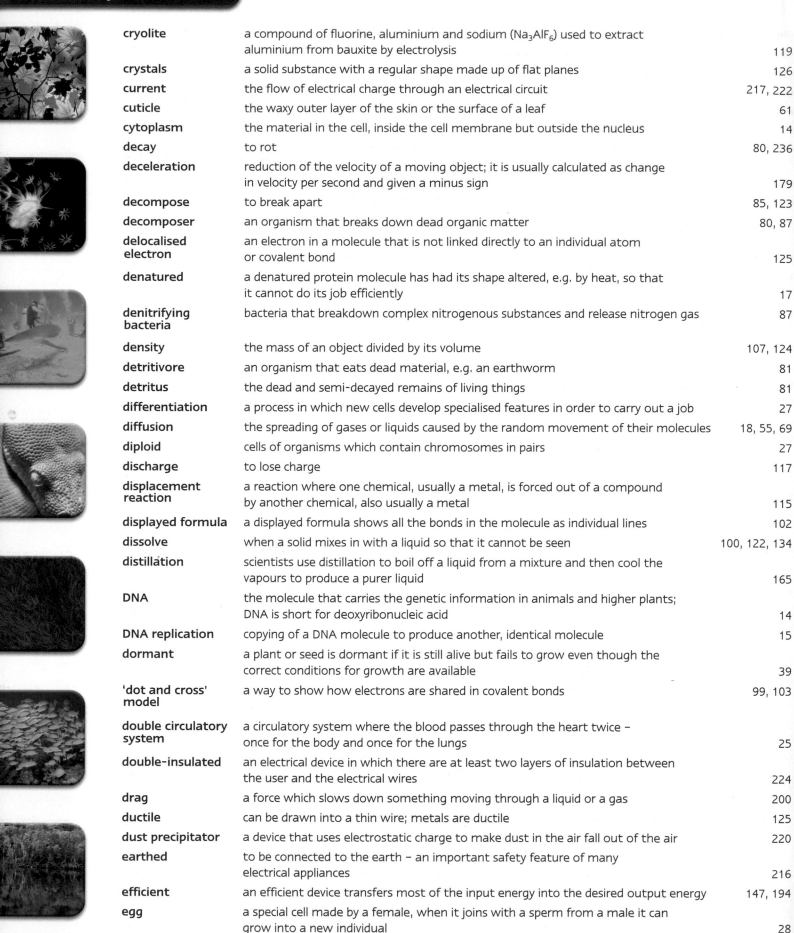

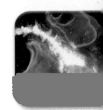

fungicide	a chemical that kills fungi	76
fuse	a special component in an electrical circuit containing a thin wire which is designed to heat up and melt if too much current flows through it, breaking the circuit	225
gamete	special cells that join to form a new individual during sexual reproduction	28
gamma	the third letter of the Greek alphabet	232, 237
gamma camera	a camera that takes pictures using gamma rays not light	235
gas exchange	the movement of gases across an exchange membrane, e.g. in the lungs of mammals gaseous exchange usually involves carbon dioxide and oxygen moving in opposite directions	19
Geiger counter	a device used to detect some types of radiation	236
gene	a length of DNA that tells growing cells how to make particular chemicals; genes help to determine the eventual structure and behaviour of an organism	14, 42
gene pool	the total number of genes available to a species in a local population	41
genetic engineering	a range of technologies that allow scientists to manipulate individual genes	42
genetic modification	a genetically modified organism is one that has had genes from another species added to it using DNA technology	42
genetically identical	having exactly the same genes, i.e. being clones	27, 44
geotropism	growing towards the centre of the earth	37
germination	the first stages of growth of a seed into a new plant	39
gestation	the time between conception and birth in humans, gestation is called pregnancy and lasts for roughly 42 weeks	35
giant ionic lattice	a large collection of ions held together by strong electrostatic charges	101
gradient	a slope or difference in measurements between two areas	177, 178
graphite	a type of carbon often used in pencils as the 'lead'	162
gravitational field strength	the force of attraction between two bodies caused by their mass; the force of gravity produced by a body depends on its mass – the larger the mass the larger the force	207
gravitational potential energy	the energy a body has because of its position in a gravitational field, e.g. an object held above the ground has gravitational potential energy that can be released if the object is dropped	204
gravity	the force of attraction between two bodies caused by their mass; the force of gravity produced by a body depends on its mass – the larger the mass the larger the force	36, 200, 207
greenhouse gas	gases like carbon dioxide and water vapour that increase the greenhouse effect	189
guard cell	cells which change shape to open or close the stomata in leaves	55
Haber process	the industrial process developed by Fritz Haber to make ammonia from nitrogen and hydrogen	121
haemoglobin	a complex chemical found in red blood cells that can combine with oxygen to help transport it around the body	23
half-life	time taken for half of the radioactive atomic nuclei in a sample of an element to break down; the shorter the half-life the more quickly a radioactive chemical decays	237, 241
halogen	a group of reactive non-metals with only one electron missing from their outer electron shell, e.g. chlorine and iodine	112
haploid number	the number of chromosomes present in the sperm or egg of a species	29
herbicide	a chemical that can kill plants, usually used to mean a chemical that kills weeds	76
herbivore	an animal that eats plants	73
hertz	a unit of frequency equal to one cycle per second	226
homologous	a matched pair of chromosomes; humans have 22 homologous pairs of chromosomes and a pair of sex chromosomes	27

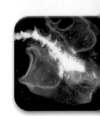

Glossary

meiosis	a specialised form of cell division that produces cells carrying half the usual number of chromosomes, these cells are called gametes and are used in sexual reproduction	29
melting point	the temperature at which a solid changes to a liquid	100
membrane	a flat sheet	14, 58
metal halide	a compound containing only a metal and a halogen atom, e.g. sodium chloride	113
metallic bond	the bond typical of metals in which electrons are shared between many atoms in a stable crystalline structure	124
microorganism	an organism that is only visible under a microscope	80
migrate	to move over long distances in a particular direction, usually applied to the movement of birds flying south for the winter	117
mineral	natural solid materials with a fixed chemical composition and structure, rocks are made of collections of minerals; mineral nutrients in our diet are things like calcium and iron, they are simple chemicals needed for health	66, 118, 142
mineral deficiency	lack of essential minerals in the diet of animals or soil of plants	69
mitochondria	cell structures that carry out aerobic respiration	15
mitosis	the process of cell division that ensures that new cells have a complete copy of inherited information	27
molecular formula	a chemical formula that shows the number and kinds of atoms in a molecule	102
molecule	a group of atoms joined together by chemical links	98, 102, 201
molten	something is molten if it has been heated to change it from a solid to a liquid	99, 116
multi-cellular	having more than one cell	27
mutation	a random change in the genotype of an organism, mutations are almost always disadvantageous	40
nano properties	the properties of materials at the nanoscale, often different to the same material's properties at the visible scale	163
nanoparticle	a particle that has at least one dimension that is smaller than 100 nanometres, a nanometre is 10^{-9} m	162
nanoscale	objects and events occurring at distances of fewer than 100 nanometres	162
nanotube	a molecule consisting of carbon atoms joined in a cylinder one to two nanometres in diameter and about a millimetre in length	162
negative ion	an ion with a negative charge	99, 115
neucleon	a particle found in the nucleus, e.g. a proton or a neutron	239
neutral	a neutral solution has a pH of 7 and is neither acid nor alkaline	95, 224
neutralise	a reaction between an acid and an alkali to produce a neutral solution	134, 144, 153
neutron	a particle found in the nucleus of an atom, it has no electrical charge and a mass of 1 atomic mass unit	95, 238, 245
newton	the unit of force	183
nitrate	a salt of nitric acid	86
nitrifying bacteria	bacteria that take in nitrogen gas and produce complex nitrogen-containing chemicals	87
nitrogen	a non-reactive gas that makes up most of the atmosphere	66, 84, 146
nitrogen-fixing bacteria	bacteria that take in nitrogen gas and produce complex nitrogen-containing chemicals	87
nitrogenous	chemicals containing nitrogen	144
non-renewable	non-renewable fuels are not being made fast enough at the moment and so will run out at some point in the future	192
nuclear	to do with the nucleus	244
nuclear transfer	moving the nucleus from one cell into another cell which has had its nucleus removed	45

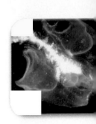

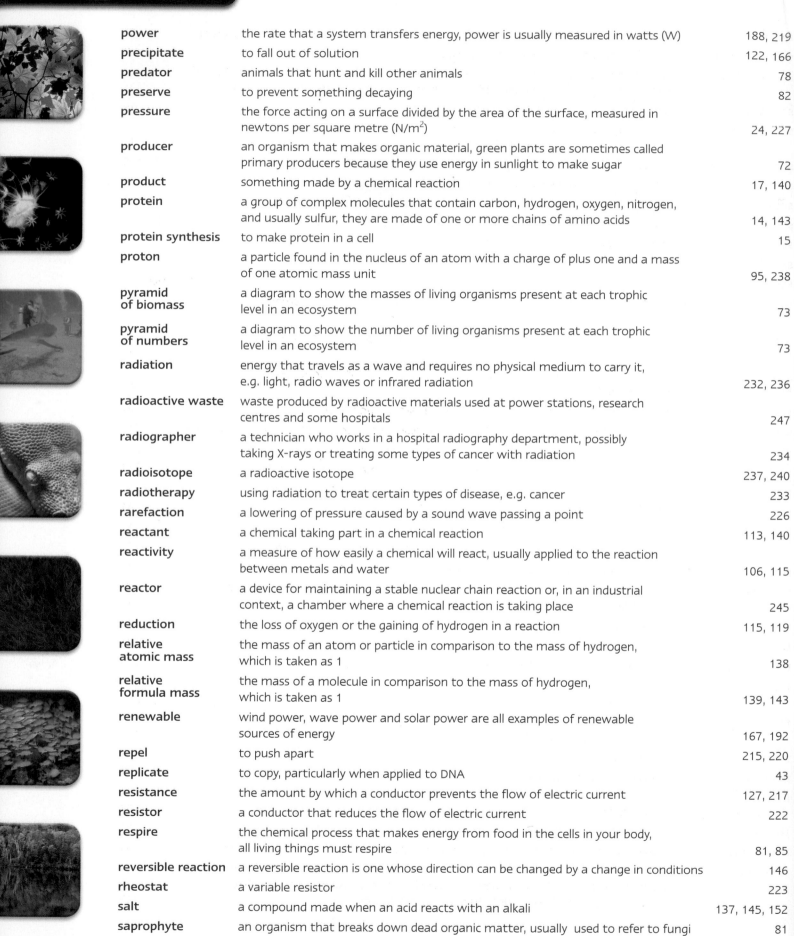

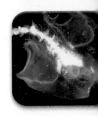

Glossary

tracer	a radioactive, or radiation-emitting, substance used in a nuclear medicine scan or other research where movement of a particular chemical is to be followed	235, 240
transition element	a metal belonging to the transition group in the periodic table	120
transpiration	the release of water vapour from a plant through the leaves	60, 64
transverse	in transverse waves, the vibration is at right angles to the direction in which the wave travels	227
trophic	the level at which an organism gets its food, primary producers are level one, primary consumers are level two and secondary consumers are level three	73
turgid	plant cells which are full of water with their walls bowed out and pushing against neighbouring cells are turgid	59
turgor pressure	the pressure exerted on the cell membrane by the cell wall when the cell is fully inflated	59
ultrasound	sounds which have too high a frequency for humans to hear (above 20 khz)	226
unicellular	containing only one cell	27
Universal indicator solution	an indicator that changes colour in solutions of different pH	134
uranium	a radioactive metal used in nuclear power stations and bombs	242, 244
urea	a white crystalline substance made by the liver to remove excess (NH$_2$) groups	87
uterus	the organ in the female where the baby grows during pregnancy, also known as the womb	20
vacuole	a sac in a cell filled with a watery solution, plant cells tend to have large vacuoles but animal cells have small ones	32
valve	something that only lets liquids pass one way	25
variable	this is something that can vary if you were in an investigation	183
variable resistor	a resistor whose resistance can change	223
variation	the existence of a range of individuals of the same group with different characteristics	29, 41
vascular bundle	a collection of xylem and phloem vessels in a plant, they can be seen in leaves as the veins	63
vein	in animals: a blood vessel carrying blood towards the heart in plants: a collection of xylem and phloem vessels clearly seen on the surface of a leaf	22, 55
velocity	velocity is the speed an object is moving in a particular direction, a change in direction or speed will change the velocity; velocity is usually measured in metres per second (m/s)	181, 205
ventricle	large muscular chamber in the heart	25
villi	a small projection on the inner surface of the gut to increase the surface area and so speed up absorption	19
volt	the international unit of electrical potential	223
voltage	the potential difference across a component or circuit	217, 223
voltmeter	a meter that measures the voltage between two points	223
watt	a unit of power, 1 watt equals 1 joule of energy being transferred per second	188
wavelength	the distance between two identical points on a wave	226
weight	the force of gravity acting on a body on Earth; weight is a force and is measured in newtons	186, 207
work	work is done when a force moves, the greater the force or the larger the distance the more work is done	186, 205
X-ray	electromagnetic radiation used by doctors to look inside a patient's body or to destroy some types of cancer cells	229, 232
xylem	cells specialised for transporting water through a plant; xylem cells have thick walls, no cytoplasm and are dead, their end walls break down and they form a continuous tube	63
yield	the ratio of product to starting materials, a high yield means that most of the starting material is converted to useful products	41, 140
zygote	a cell produced when a male and female gamete join	29